NEW DIRECTIONS
FOR METHODOLOGY OF
SOCIAL AND
BEHAVIORAL SCIENCE

Number 5 • 1980

NEW DIRECTIONS FOR METHODOLOGY OF SOCIAL AND BEHAVIORAL SCIENCE

A Quarterly Sourcebook
Donald W. Fiske, Editor-in-Chief

Number 5, 1980

Quantitative Assessment of Research Domains

Robert Rosenthal
Guest Editor

Jossey-Bass Inc., Publishers
San Francisco • Washington • London

QUANTITATIVE ASSESSMENT OF RESEARCH DOMAINS
New Directions for Methodology of Social and Behavioral Science
Number 5, 1980
Robert Rosenthal, Guest Editor

New Directions for Methodology of Social and Behavioral Science is published quarterly by Jossey-Bass Inc., Publishers. Subscriptions are available at the regular rate for institutions, libraries, and agencies of $30 for one year. Individuals may subscribe at the special professional rate of $18 for one year.

Correspondence:
Subscriptions, single-issue orders, change of address notices, undelivered copies, and other correspondence should be sent to *New Directions* Subscriptions, Jossey-Bass Inc., Publishers, 433 California Street, San Francisco, California 94104. Editorial correspondence should be sent to the Editor-in-Chief, Donald W. Fiske, University of Chicago, Chicago, Illinois 60637.

Library of Congress Catalogue Card Number LC 80-81899

Cover design by Willi Baum

Manufactured in the United States of America

Contents

Editor's Notes

In the behavioral and social sciences, it has become almost obligatory for us to end our articles with clarion calls for further research. Yet it seems fair to say that we have been better at issuing such calls than at knowing what to do with the answers. There are many areas of the behavioral and social sciences for which we do in fact have available the results of many studies, all addressing essentially the same question. Our summaries of the results of these sets of studies, however, have not been nearly as informative as they might have been, either with respect to summarized significance levels or with respect to summarized effect sizes. Even the best reviews of research by the most sophisticated workers have rarely told us more about each study of a set of studies than the direction of the relationship between the variables investigated and if it did or did not reach a given p level (Feldman, 1971; Luborsky, Chandler, Auerbach, Cohen, and Bachrach, 1971; Taveggia, 1974).

This state of affairs is beginning to change. More and more reviews of the literature are moving from the traditional, literary format to the quantitative format (Cooper and Rosenthal, 1980). It is the purpose of this sourcebook to help in this process of change by making readily available the foundations of the various procedures developed for the quantitative assessment of research domains.

The first three chapters present the conceptual and practical foundations of some of the most useful methods for summarizing research areas while the remaining chapters present detailed applications and illustrations of the principles set foward in the first part.

If one were to trace historically the development of the movement to quantify runs of studies, one might well begin with Fisher (1938) for his thinking about the combination of the significance levels of independent studies, continue with Mosteller and Bush (1954) for their broadening of the Fisher perspective both in (1) introducing several new methods of combining independent probability levels to social and behavioral scientists, and (2) showing that effect sizes as well as significance levels could be usefully combined, and end in the present day with an expanding number of investigators including all the contributors to this volume and their colleagues cited in the bibliographies.

David Pillemer and Richard Light open the volume with their chapter emphasizing the scientific benefits to be derived from careful analysis of the variation found in a run of studies with respect to both significance levels and effect sizes. Furthermore, they tell us *how* we may approach such analyses. Next, Gene Glass describes various procedures for converting results of studies to standard units of effect size. The basic unit, $\triangle_{A-B}$, related to Cohen's d (1969, 1977), turns out to be estimable under a wide variety of conditions of research and reporting procedures. Then, Robert Rosenthal describes various procedures for summarizing significance levels as well as some procedures for dealing with the "file drawer problem"—the extreme view of which is that the journals are filled with the 5 percent of the studies that show Type I errors, while the file drawers back at the lab are filled with the 95 percent of the studies that show nonsignificant results.

Mary Lee Smith's chapter opens the section on applications and illustrations of the procedures presented in the first three chapters with a summary of a research integration of several hundred studies of the outcome of psychotherapy. This research integration finally settles the ancient question: Does psychotherapy work? Judith Hall relates what the literature has to say about sex differences in skill at encoding and decoding nonverbal cues. She tells not only what now *is* known but also what should have been known years earlier had reviewers employed more systematic, quantitative methods for summarizing research. In the final chapter, Robert Rosenthal and Donald Rubin summarize the results of several hundred studies of interpersonal expectancy effects emphasizing both the combining of independent probabilities and the estimation of effect sizes, the latter by means of sampling procedures.

The volume ends with a brief annotated bibliography designed to give readers ready access to other examples of the quantitative assessment of research domains (or meta-analyses, as Glass has referred to these efforts).

It is our hope that this volume will contribute to the trend toward more rigorous summarization and integration of research literatures. We look forward to the day when behavioral and social science journals that publish reviews of literature will require, at the very least, of each summarizer an estimate of overall effect size, a combined probability level, a statement of tolerance for future null results, and indications of possible moderator variables affecting the size of the effect.

Robert Rosenthal
Guest Editor

References

Cohen, J. *Statistical Power Analysis for the Behavioral Sciences.* New York: Academic Press, 1969.

Cohen, J. *Statistical Power Analysis for the Behavioral Sciences.* (rev. ed.) New York: Academic Press, 1977.

Cooper, H. M., and Rosenthal, R. "Statistical Versus Traditional Procedures for Summarizing Research Findings." *Psychological Bulletin,* 1980, *87,* 442–449.

Feldman, K. A. "Using the Work of Others: Some Observations on Reviewing and Integrating." *Sociology of Education,* 1971, *44,* 86–102.

Fisher, R. A. *Statistical Methods for Research Workers.* (7th ed.) London: Oliver and Boyd, 1938.

Luborsky, L., Chandler, M., Auerbach, A. H., Cohen, J., and Bachrach, M. H. "Factors Influencing the Outcome of Psychotherapy: A Review of Quantitative Research." *Psychological Bulletin,* 1971, *75,* 145–185.

Mosteller, F. M., and Bush, R. R. "Selected Quantitative Techniques." In G. Lindzey (Ed.), *Handbook of Social Psychology.* Vol. 1: *Theory and Method.* Cambridge, Mass.: Addison-Wesley, 1954.

Taveggia, T. C. "Resolving Research Controversy Through Empirical Cumulation: Toward Reliable Sociological Knowledge." *Sociological Methods and Research,* 1974, *2,* 395–407.

Robert Rosenthal is professor of social psychology at Harvard University. His major research interests include interpersonal expectancy effects, nonverbal communication, and social research methods. He is the author of Experimenter Effects in Behavioral Research *and co-author with Lenore Jacobson of* Pygmalion in the Classroom.

Any one study should be examined in the context of other, related studies. The complexity of findings compels us to search for structure.

Benefiting from Variation in Study Outcomes

David B. Pillemer
Richard J. Light

The literature review in social science appears to be in the process of transformation and improvement. Traditionally, investigators developing state-of-the-art overviews of research on a specific topic have relied almost exclusively on two procedures. One is to present narrative descriptions of different studies. The second is to find the most common outcome and report this as the best "answer" available. But this type of review leaves many questions unanswered. Which studies should be included? How should varied and sometimes conflicting results be dealt with? Such decisions have often appeared subjective and even haphazard.

Over the past decade, several researchers have commented on how unsystematically knowledge accumulates in social science (Glass, 1976, 1977; Kulik, Kulik, and Cohen, 1979; Light, 1979; Light and Smith, 1971; Pillemer and Light, 1980; Rosenthal, 1968, 1969, 1978). They have taken a first cut at developing or using procedures for synthesizing information. These efforts have a common goal: to draw systematic summary information from a set of studies that examine a similar question. For example, Kulik, Kulik, and

This work has been facilitated by long-term grants from the National Institute of Education and the Spencer Foundation.

Cohen (1979) pulled together dozens of studies of a certain method of "personalized instruction," and concluded that this method usually outperforms more traditional classroom teaching.

Synthesizing the results of several studies may inform both short-term social policy and longer-term future research. For research findings to help policy, they must be understandable and provide "answers." In an ideal world, these answers are clear-cut: either a treatment or program works or it does not. But in the real world, answers are rarely this neat. A program may work in some instances and not in others. When it does work, its effects may be marginal. For example, the question, "What are the effects of Title I legislation?" does not have a simple answer. Certain Title I programs work; others seem to fail, and still others have no effect. Title I success depends on a variety of factors, such as participant characteristics, and how the money is distributed.

This chapter is motivated by our belief that explaining conflicting results can have a high payoff. Elsewhere we have argued that conflicting results should not dissuade an analyst from trying to synthesize. On the contrary, it is just these situations that may be most fruitful for synthesis. If each of one hundred studies finds that a program has the same positive effect, then reporting an overall finding is easy. It will also probably not be very interesting, as this finding will be well known.

A key benefit of synthesis is a clearer understanding of the complexities in the real world. When does a treatment work, and when does it fail? Synthesis may succeed in identifying and summarizing setting by treatment interactions, indicating where and why a treatment is likely to be successful. The important goal of obtaining single overall estimates of treatment effectiveness, and their statistical significance, is considered in the chapters by Rosenthal and by Glass. We hope that an analyst will find both lines of thought helpful when undertaking a complex analysis.

Common Sources of Variation in Study Outcomes

It is not always possible to explain conflicting findings. But sometimes the variation among different studies can be partitioned into components that help us understand why outcomes differ. We suggest four such possibilities.

First, *similarly labeled treatments or programs may in fact differ in important ways.* Just because several research reports describe a program as Head Start, or Follow Through, or Upward Bound, one should not assume these are in fact the same program. So an initial step in synthesizing outcomes should be to see whether a set of programs with the same name is in fact providing the same services. In the process, we may discover program variations that are especially effective or ineffective, leading to valuable substantive insights. For example, one analysis of public school effectiveness indicated that the most effective schools had better paid and more experienced teachers, and smaller classes than the average school (Klitgaard, 1975).

Second, assurances that programs with the same title are in fact similar will not eliminate conflicts. A program does not operate in a vacuum. A treatment may be more or less effective depending on who participates in it, where it is administered, or some other situational factor. These *setting-by-treatment* interactions are known to be quite common in social and educational programs. To provide one example, offering rewards to children contingent upon correct performance on IQ tests is effective in raising the scores of initially low scoring subjects, but has little effect upon the performance of higher scorers (Clingman and Fowler, 1976). So this "reward" treatment is not universally effective, but rather depends to some degree upon the characteristics of the children receiving it. These seeming inconsistencies may help us to decide where and when a program is likely to succeed.

A third potential source of conflicting results is the way different studies were designed. *The type of research design employed in a study can strongly influence the outcome.* One study characteristic that has received particular attention is how people are assigned to treatment and control groups (Campbell and Boruch, 1975). For example, Gilbert, Light, and Mosteller (1975) report a strong relationship between the use of randomization and reported outcomes in studies of the effects of shunt operations in medicine.

Other design characteristics can influence findings, such as the length of time a treatment is implemented. For example, there are a number of short-term experiments and several longer-term studies investigating the effects of television violence on children's attitudes and behavior. The short-term studies generally show that watching violence increases children's aggression, while at least longer-term study demonstrates increased aggressiveness in children assigned to a nonviolent TV diet (Leifer, Gordon, and Graves, 1974). It would not be surprising if the outcomes depended at least partially upon the tenure of the treatment. While short-term experiments are superimposed upon existing behaviors, long-term restrictions on children's violence viewing disrupt children's normal viewing patterns. The children assigned to the nonviolent viewing condition may have reacted angrily and aggressively to the withholding of their favorite violent programs. These conflicting research findings have a key policy implication. Since the length of the treatment may be important, any regulations limiting television violence should be carefully monitored over time for unintended long-term consequences.

A fourth source of conflict involves the analysis strategies used in different studies. Even if all the analyses are done correctly, the *particular analysis procedures that are used may be related to outcomes,* and create artificial conflicts. For example, the unit or level of analysis may differ across studies. Whether an analysis is conducted at the pupil, class, or school level dramatically influences estimates of the strength of relationships in evaluations such as Project Follow Through (Haney, 1974). Judy Singer has analyzed data from the National Day Care Study (1979) and shown that the strength of the relationship between a child outcome variable and several day care policy variables differs when the analysis is done at the classroom level as opposed to the individual child level. A general rule here is that for any data set, the more highly aggregated the unit of analysis, the stronger the relationship (or larger the R^2) will be. For example, the National Day Care Study consistently found higher R^2s for analyses conducted at the "center level" than at the "child level."

There are, then, several possible explanations for conflicting findings. The key idea underlying all of them is that investigating conflict can sometimes reveal important information about program effectiveness that would *not* be available from a single, large, well conducted evaluation. In this sense, having several small studies may actually be preferable to having a single large one. The conflicts act as warning flags to an investigator, suggesting that it may be useful to look for setting-by-treatment interactions, to question if a similar program was actually implemented at different sites, or to examine variation in design characteristics and analysis strategies. Light (1979) gives some specific numerical examples. Taking this perspective, variation among study outcomes can be a useful, constructive, information-laden occurrence.

Approaches to Examining Variation in Study Outcomes

A number of statistical approaches are useful for examining variation among similar studies. The procedures use statistical information routinely reported in journal articles, and none of them is computationally difficult. In this section, we present three approaches to studying variation in outcomes: examining variation in significance levels, variation in effect sizes, and variation between similarly labeled treatments. Our focus here is on general characteristics of the procedures, and how each can be useful.

Variation in Significance Levels. Suppose that several independent studies each compare two treatments, that the treatments are similar across studies, and that the group differences are tested statistically in each instance. A number of statistical procedures are available for combining the separate statistical tests into a single overall test. An example of their use appears in Rosenthal and Rubin (1978; also their chapter in this volume) who report that a combined test of the effects of researchers' (or teachers') expectancies on subjects' (or pupils') performance across 345 independent studies produced a highly significant overall result.

Significance levels associated with separate studies can also give clues about whether there is unusual variation in study outcomes. Consider an example from a U.S. Office of Education analysis of Title I effectiveness, discussed by Light and Smith (1971). Of 189 total observations, fifty-eight classrooms were significantly improved and fifty lost ground, with eighty-one classrooms virtually unchanged.

What does this *distribution* of significant outcomes suggest? First, it is apparent that the number of significant changes in both directions greatly exceeds what chance would predict. If Title I were consistently having *no* effect, we would expect about 5 percent statistically significant outcomes because of sampling error. In this analysis over 50 percent of the outcomes were significant.

Second, it is important that the significant outcomes are almost evenly split between gains and losses. One might be tempted to conclude that these conflicting outcomes cancel each other out, leading to an inference of no program effect. While an overall combined significance test could lead to this conclusion, it would be misleading since the distribution of outcomes does not reflect random variation around a "true" effect of zero. A more useful policy conclusion to describe reality is that Title I programs vary in their effects; some help, some hurt, and some make no difference at all.

These Title I data illustrate how the distribution of significance levels can signal that unusual variation in outcomes exists. As a follow-up, when outcomes conflict, the analyst should try to find out why. Sometimes this appears clear-cut. For example, Hall (1978; and her chapter in this volume) analyzes seventy-five studies of sex differences in ability to decode nonverbal information. The distribution of significance levels clearly indicates nonrandom variation: twenty-four of the seventy-five studies produced statistically significant sex differences. Further, examining the direction of the effects indicates that twenty-three of the twenty-four significant differences favor females. Hall concludes that women's superiority on this type of task is primarily responsible for the significant outcomes.

But often the data are less clear. When nonrandom variation turns up, there are many candidates for explanation. Setting-by-treatment interactions may be large, far larger than the main program effect. Or the design characteristics may be related to their outcomes (Grace, Muench, and Chalmers, 1966). An analyst must develop hypotheses about what might explain excessive variation in study outcomes, and systematically examine those hypotheses. We suggest some ways to do this in the last part of this chapter.

Relying only on significance levels to identify unusual variation in outcomes has several potential drawbacks. One is the "file drawer" problem that has been discussed by Robert Rosenthal (1979; see also his chapter in this volume). There may be an overrepresentation of statistically significant results reported in the literature because significant outcomes are more likely to be published than nonsignificant results. This being the case, there may be file drawers filled with well done but nonsignificant studies which, if included in a data synthesis, would result in a more balanced distribution of outcomes.

One way of handling this problem is to estimate the number of nonsignificant outcomes that would be necessary in order for the number of significant outcomes to fall into the range predicted by chance. If this number seems excessive even for liberal estimates of unpublished studies, an analyst can be more confident that the significant outcomes have substantive importance.

It may also be possible to explain the significant outcomes by identifying a crucial background variable. For example, Hall (1978) points out that, even if there were many unpublished studies measuring ability to decode nonverbal information that were not statistically significant, this would not negate the conclusion that virtually all of the significant findings favored females over males.

Before leaving this topic, we want to remind readers of a simple but crucial point bearing on an outcome being statistically significant. The point is that sample size matters. An effect that is nonsignificant in a small study may be highly significant in a large study. For this reason, we must be very careful not to focus *only* on statistical significance. Program A and program B may both improve children's reading readiness by five points, yet only A will be significant because more children participated. Several investigators have chosen to deal with this problem by moving away from statistical significance as the key indicator of success, and focusing instead on effect size.

Variation in Effect Sizes. What do we mean by *effect size?* We will adopt a definition similar to that used by Rosenthal and others in this volume. When comparing two treatments or a treatment to a control, the size of the effect is simply the difference between the means of the two groups divided by the within-group standard deviation assumed common to the two populations. This is the *"d"* statistic described by Cohen (1977). Thus, the effect is expressed in standard deviation units, enabling direct comparisons among studies differing in sample size or other characteristics. One study might have an effect of 1.2 standard deviation units and another study .6 standard deviation units. The effect size in the first study is twice as large as in the second study, independent of the sample sizes.

If an effect size is reported or can be computed for each of several studies, the average effect size for the entire set can easily be calculated. For example, Smith and Glass (1977) computed the average effect size of psychotherapy across 400 separate studies to be .68 of a standard deviation (see also the chapter by Smith in this volume).

As with significance levels, effect sizes can also serve the dual purpose of signaling unusual variation in outcomes. It may be useful to examine the *distribution* of effect sizes across the set of studies. If the variation appears normal, and does not have worrisome outliers, an analyst may be more confident that the studies are all estimating the same population mean. If, however, unusual variation exists, an analyst will want to search for explanatory factors. For example, Glass (1977) related psychotherapy effects to the number of months after therapy that effects were measured. These analyses indicated the effect of therapy diminishes as the time lag increases. So time lag was one variable that helped to explain differences among study outcomes. (Rosenthal, 1978, describes and Pillemer and Light, 1980, discuss a statistical procedure, known as the "blocking technique," that is useful for detecting unusual variation in effect sizes.)

Variation Among Similarly Labeled Treatments. Examining variation in either significance levels or effect sizes focuses on differences among outcomes. For example, if reading program A is compared to a control in each of two independent studies, the effect sizes can be compared to see if the two studies generally agree as to program A's effectiveness. However, it can happen that two *versions* of program A can be very different, yet this difference will not be detected using the techniques described so far.

Light and Smith (1971) discuss a "cluster approach" to data synthesis that addresses this issue. The basic idea is straightforward. Before combining a set of similarly labeled programs for synthesis, an analyst must first decide that the programs are in fact similar enough to justify combining them. Ten "developmental day care" programs may sound like a homogeneous group, but a day care center can name its curriculum anything it chooses. To call all the programs "the treatment," and to then aggregate across the ten studies, could gloss over important differences.

The cluster approach adds a time-consuming step to the data aggregation process. Light and Smith propose a series of "hurdles" that must be passed before subgroups can be combined: either the means, variances, subject-by-treatment interactions, relationships between dependent variables and covariates, and contextual effects must be similar, or appropriate statistical adjustments must be made before combining similarly labeled treatments. The extra time and effort have a payoff only if differences between similarly labeled treatments are relatively common. In the social sciences, there is ample evidence that this is so. For example, Smith and Bissell (1970) outline several important differences among programs titled Head Start.

An attractive feature of comparing similarly labeled treatments, in addition to strengthening the inferences from combined data, is that unusually effective or ineffective programs may be identified. When this happens, a search for explanatory factors may lead to substantive insights about program effectiveness. For example, a particularly effective Head Start program may have an extremely high staff-to-child ratio or an innovative curriculum. Or, all particularly effective day care centers may be found to care for children in small groups.

To obtain these benefits, we must be able to identify unusual performances, or "outliers." It is easy to array similarly labeled programs by their average performance, and to select the highest or lowest scoring programs. One must be careful, however, since an isolated high or low average does not by itself tell us that the program was responsible (Klitgaard, 1978). Some scores will appear in the tails of a distribution of outcomes simply because of random variation. Further, the performance of program participants may depend upon a variety of factors (for instance, background of participants) other than the program itself. How can we tease out unusually successful or unsuccessful programs from these other influences?

A considerable amount of methodological work has been addressed to this question. Klitgaard (1978) provides an excellent summary of statistical approaches. His concluding comments neatly capture the importance of trying to identify unusual programs:

> Looking for the best may be a tentative and uncertain business, but it is also a useful one. Outliers may embody techniques that can be copied elsewhere. They may offer clues to the understanding of little-fathomed processes operating throughout the system, and they may inhibit simplistic generalizations based on group averages. Looking for excep-

> tions should be part of all statistical evaluations of public policies. Although a statistical search for unusual performances can only be a prelude to detailed case studies and not a substitute for them, it helps the scholar and the policymaker know where to focus their attention (p. 546).

Identifying Explanatory Factors

To benefit from discrepancies among studies, we must repeatedly ask the question, "What may explain the different outcomes?" Trying to answer this forces us to organize a systematic inquiry. We suggest here three specific ways to seek out and confirm explanations for conflicting outcomes.

Relating Background Variables to Outcomes. One strategy involves coding information about participants' background characteristics (such as SES) and design characteristics of the research (for example, method of assigning subjects to groups) and relating this information to study outcomes. It is surprising how quickly certain relationships may become clearer, and outcomes that seemed at first to conflict suddenly make more sense. The work of Judith Hall, mentioned earlier, used this strategy. She related several features of each study to the size of the effect of sex differences in decoding nonverbal cues. These features included both background characteristics of the participants, and research design descriptions. Her findings were interesting. For example, she found no relationship between participant's age and effect size, while the year in which the study was conducted turned out to be important (more recent studies tended to show the largest effects). An analyst could probe further to determine the cause of this latter relationship. Hall (1978, p. 854) feels that the relationship between year of study and effect size is "most likely due to a combination of more precise measuring instruments and more powerful data analysis."

Comparing Extreme Outcomes. A second strategy follows Klitgaard's (1978) suggestion "to use the unusual as a guide to the usual," since "the unusually successful (or unsuccessful) may provide a clearer picture of processes operating to a lesser extent elsewhere" (p. 531). Comparing extremely successful programs to particularly unsuccessful ones may produce a list of other clear differences between them. We hope the list will be kept short. For example, comparing a successful Title I program to one that failed miserably may point out differences in staffing, expenditures, or curricula. Notice also that since as few as two programs may be involved at this initial stage, an analyst may try to obtain information beyond that presented in published reports, to develop as thorough a body of information as possible.

When a few key explanatory factors have been identified, an analyst can form specific hypotheses about how they influence outcomes. For instance, one might expect staff-to-child ratio to influence Head Start effectiveness, but there may also be complex interactions between this variable and others, such as amount of money spent per child or total number of children in the program.

The hypotheses can be evaluated in two ways. One is to examine them using data from less extreme studies. For example, if staff-to-child ratio in Head Start is universally important, there should be some evidence of this across the entire range of study outcomes. In fact, since public policies or regulations will often influence the usual more than the unusual, this step can be critical.

A second way of examining these hypotheses is to build them into future controlled experiments. Potentially important variables identified post hoc from existing programs can sometimes be *systematically* varied in a future experiment. The National Day Care Study (1979) illustrates this. The Administration for Children, Youth, and Families analyzed many studies of day care curricula in 1974 and isolated three key policy variables as distinguishing the best centers from the worst: staff to child ratio, staff training, and group size. ACYF then funded a large investigation, including both a randomized field trial and an observational study, centered around these three variables. The results were that one (group size) was extremely important, one (staff training) was moderately important, and the last (staff to child ratio) was quite marginal. This effort illustrates the usefulness of first generating hypotheses using outliers, and then building better follow up investigations that test the hypotheses.

Considering the Usual. A third strategy looks at what is typical. Focusing on atypical programs should not deter an analyst from examining the major bulk of the studies for background features related to outcome differences. First, the fact that a study *outcome* falls in the middle of a distribution does not indicate that the *program* is typical. It is possible that a highly successful program or curriculum is paired with unusually needy participants, or poor resources, resulting in a mediocre final performance level. In these instances, an analyst would ideally want to adjust for some background factors before searching for effective or ineffective programs (see Klitgaard, 1978, for further discussion). A typical program may appear quite atypical after adjustments are made for background characteristics related to outcomes.

Investing resources to study programs that have roughly average outcomes can be valuable in another way. Focusing on extremes puts our emphasis on identifying program or participant differences in order to explain divergent findings. But in a large synthesis, involving many potential background variables, the other side of the coin is important as well. Examining studies with similar outcomes may be useful in identifying *inoperative* variables. For example, suppose that ten Head Start programs produce relatively consistent results. Suppose that while the program curricula and participants are quite similar, the formal educational level of the teachers varies dramatically across centers. This fact by itself would not *prove* that teacher education is unimportant, since it may interact with other measured or unmeasured variables. But it would strongly suggest that teacher education should not be our number one candidate for a variable that will explain outcome differences. Since in education and the social sciences there are usually enormous numbers of variables that we think might be important, this process of looking at typical outcomes can help to limit the field for first-cut analyses and study designs.

Context in a Complex World

This exposition is built upon the assumption that for science to be cumulative, any one study should be looked at in the context of other related studies, rather than standing alone. Perhaps an analyst looking at a group of studies is rather like an artist looking at a complex painting on a canvas. She could look at each of the swirls and brush strokes singly, or she could stand back and try to put each mark in the context provided by its neighbors. We believe that when a social scientist examines variation among studies, it is done in this spirit of building a context, and that the context in turn enhances the richness and value of information from any one study.

But looking at context is difficult. It involves tying outcomes to details about how each study was done, and who participated. It may also seem optimistic. One may ask why we are not content to simply accept outcomes as they are reported by others, and why we keep wanting to adjust for this and control for that. Our answer is *not* that we expect to explain *all* variation in outcomes if only the proper adjustments are made. Rather, we believe that in a world where program effects *are* complex, and multivariate, and interactive, it is precisely this complexity that forces a scientist to search for whatever structure may exist.

References

Campbell, D. T., and Boruch, R. "Making the Case for Randomized Assignment to Treatments by Considering the Alternatives: Six Ways in Which Quasi-Experimental Evaluations in Compensatory Education Tend to Underestimate Effects." In C. A. Bennett and A. A. Lumsdaine (Eds.), *Evaluation and Experiment.* New York: Academic Press, 1975.

Clingman, J., and Fowler, R. I. "The Effects of Primary Reward on the I.Q. Performance of Grade-School Children as a Function of Initial I.Q. Level." *Journal of Applied Behavior Analysis,* 1976, *9,* 19–23.

Cohen, J. *Statistical Power Analysis for the Behavioral Sciences.* (Rev. ed.) New York: Academic Press, 1977.

Gilbert, J. P., Light, R. J., and Mosteller, F. "Assessing Social Innovations: An Empirical Base for Policy." In C. A. Bennett and A. A. Lumsdaine (Eds.), *Evaluation and Experiment.* New York: Academic Press, 1975.

Glass, G. V. "Primary, Secondary, and Meta-Analysis of Research." *Educational Researcher,* 1976, *5,* 3–8.

Glass, G. V. "Integrating Findings: The Meta-Analysis of Research." *Review of Research in Education,* 1977, *5,* 351–379.

Grace, N. D., Muench, H., and Chalmers, T. C. "The Present Status of Shunts for Portal Hypertension in Cirrhosis." *Gastroenterology,* 1966, *50,* 684–691.

Hall, J. A. "Gender Effects in Decoding Nonverbal Cues." *Psychological Bulletin,* 1978, *85,* 845–857.

Haney, W. "Units of Analysis Issues in the Evaluation of Project Follow Through." Document prepared for U.S. Office of Education, Contract No. OEC-0-74-0394. Cambridge, Mass.: The Huron Institute, 1974.

Klitgaard, R. "Going Beyond the Mean in Educational Evaluation." *Public Policy,* 1975, *23,* 59–79.

Klitgaard, R. "Identifying Exceptional Performers." *Policy Analysis,* Fall 1978, pp. 529-547.

Kulik, J. A., Kulik, C. C., and Cohen, P. A. "A Meta-Analysis of Outcome Studies of Keller's Personalized System of Instruction." *American Psychologist,* 1979, *34,* 307-318.

Leifer, A., Gordon, N., and Graves, S. "Children's Television: More Than Mere Entertainment." *Harvard Educational Review,* 1974, *44,* 213-245.

Light, R. J. "Capitalizing on Variation: How Conflicting Research Findings Can Be Helpful for Policy." *Educational Researcher,* 1979, *8,* 3-8.

Light, R. J., and Smith, P. V. "Accumulating Evidence: Procedures for Resolving Contradictions Among Different Studies." *Harvard Educational Review,* 1971, *41,* 429-471.

National Day Care Study. *Children at the Center.* Cambridge, Mass.: Abt Books, 1979.

Pillemer, D. B., and Light, R. J. "Using the Results of Randomized Experiments to Construct Social Programs: Three Caveats." In *Evaluation Studies Review Annual.* Beverly Hills, Calif.: Sage, 1979.

Pillemer, D. B., and Light, R. J. "Synthesizing Outcomes: How To Use Research Evidence from Many Studies." *Harvard Educational Review,* 1980, *50,* 176-195.

Rosenthal, R. "Experimenter Expectancy and the Reassuring Nature of the Null Hypothesis Decision Procedure." *Psychological Bulletin Monograph Supplement,* 1968, *70,* 30-47.

Rosenthal, R. "Interpersonal Expectations: Effects of the Experimenter's Hypothesis." In R. Rosenthal and R. L. Rosnow (Eds.), *Artifact in Behavioral Research.* New York: Academic Press, 1969.

Rosenthal, R. "Combining Results of Independent Studies." *Psychological Bulletin,* 1978, *85,* 185-193.

Rosenthal, R. "The 'File Drawer Problem' and Tolerance for Null Results." *Psychological Bulletin,* 1979, *86,* 638-641.

Rosenthal, R., and Rubin, D. B. "Interpersonal Expectancy Effects: The First 345 Studies." *The Behavioral and Brain Sciences,* 1978, *3,* 377-415.

Smith, M. S., and Bissell, J. "The Impact of Head Start." *Harvard Educational Review,* 1970, *40,* 51-104.

Smith, M. L., and Glass, G. V. "Meta-Analysis of Psychotherapy Outcome Studies." *American Psychologist,* 1977, *32,* 752-760.

David B. Pillemer is assistant professor of psychology, Wellesley College and research associate in education, Harvard University. His current research interests include cognitive development in children and developing strategies for synthesizing social science research findings.

Richard J. Light is professor of education and public policy at Harvard University. His interests focus on quantitative methods for evaluating and improving social programs, especially education and human services. He is chairman of a National Academy of Sciences Panel on measuring outcomes of demonstration projects, and serves on the Panel on Evaluation Research of the Social Science Research Council.

Standardized effects can be compared, even when a set of studies has diverse types of data.

Summarizing Effect Sizes

Gene V Glass

Experimental studies produce estimates of effects. A reasonable definition, stemming from least-squares estimation theory, of the comparative effect of treatments A and B is the difference in the expected values of the dependent variable, y, under A and B, that is, effect = $\mu_A - \mu_B$. When the dependent variable, such as "learning" or "anxiety," is measured differently in different experiments (perhaps because of arbitrary differences in the expression of scales or even because of genuine differences in techniques of measurement), then comparability of effects can be achieved by standardizing $\mu_A - \mu_B$ by a scale factor, for instance the standard deviation. The standardized comparative effect is a useful basic unit of an integrative analysis that attempts to describe and analyze the findings of many experiments. Symbolically it can be denoted as follows:

$$\Delta_{A-B} = \frac{\mu_A - \mu_B}{\sigma_y} \qquad (1)$$

Suppose that four experiments were performed in which either nialomide or iproniazid was compared with a placebo for efficacy in relieving depression. Three of the experiments measured outcomes with the MMPI D

Preparation of this chapter was supported in part by a grant from the National Institute of Education (No. NIE-G-78-0148). Robert Rosenthal gave many helpful suggestions on drafts of the manuscript.

scale; the fourth study used the Beck Depression Inventory. Suppose the following results were obtained. (The data are hypothetical, but the findings are close to those reported in Smith, Glass, and Miller, 1980).

Study No.	*Comparison*	*Test*	*Means*	*St. Dev.*	Δ_{A-B}
1	Nialomide vs. Placebo	MMPI	70.10– 70.50	9.50	– .04
2	Nialomide vs. Placebo	MMPI	61.45– 62.31	11.25	– .08
3	Iproniazid vs. Placebo	MMPI	60.21– 65.15	7.80	– .63
4	Iproniazid vs. Placebo	Beck	110.75–121.45	20.50	– .52

In the above data, the average effect of nialomide is – .06, that is, six-hundredths standard deviation superior to a placebo; the average effect of iproniazid is – .58, more than a half standard deviation.

The Δ index of experimental effect seems reasonable and useful for integrating experimental findings. But many questions about it must be addressed: (1) How should Δ_{A-B} be estimated from samples? (2) Which standardizing variance should be used when many different ones exist? (3) How can Δ be estimated when y has been reduced to a dichotomy in the report of an experiment? (4) What special problems arise when Δs come from many experiments in which experimental treatments A, B, C, . . . are compared in various combinations? (5) How might Δs be integrated when the independent variable can be described by a simple quantitative scale (amount of drug, percent reinforcement, size of group, and the like)?

Estimation of Δ

Given that,

$$\Delta_{A-B} = \frac{\mu_A - \mu_B}{\sigma_y}, \tag{2}$$

and assuming for the moment an understanding of which of many possible choices of σ_y is implied, the intuitively reasonable estimator of Δ is

$$\hat{\Delta}_{A-B} = \frac{\bar{y}_A - \bar{y}_B}{s_y}, \tag{3}$$

where the sample means are conventionally defined and s_y is the square root of the *unbiased* estimator of σ_y^2. Hedges (1979) showed the error of intuition with regard to (3), and derived the maximum likelihood estimator of Δ assuming normality and a single sample estimate of σ_y based on k degrees of freedom. The maximum likelihood estimator of Δ can differ substantially from $\hat{\Delta}$ in (3) when samples are small. Hedges tabulated the ratio of $\hat{\Delta}$ and the maximum likelihood estimate of Δ for $k = 2, \ldots, 50$. When $k = 4$, for example, the ratio of $\hat{\Delta}$ to the maximum likelihood estimator of Δ is 1.25, that is, Δ is 25 percent too large. The ratio reaches 1.04 for $k = 20$ and falls to 1.02 for $k = 50$. But for small sample results, $\hat{\Delta}$ should be corrected according to Hedges's calculations.

Choice of a Standardizing Variance

The choice of the standard deviation with which to scale the differences between group means to determine Δ is crucial. Various choices can result in substantial differences in effect size.

There are many more aspects to the problem of selecting an appropriate standardizing σ_y for Δ than can be dealt with here. (See McGaw and Glass, in press, for an extended discussion of the problem.) Three topics will be discussed in this section: (a) standardizing effects by "control group" variance; (b) finding a standardizing variance for studies without "control groups"; (c) selecting a standardizing variance in factorial experimental designs.

(a) Standardizing Effects by "Control Group" Variance. The definition of Δ appears uncomplicated, but heterogeneous group variances cause difficulties. Suppose that experimental and control groups have means and standard deviations as follows:

	Experimental	*Control*
Means	$\bar{y}_E = 52$	$\bar{y}_C = 50$
Standard Deviations	$s_E = 2$	$s_C = 10$

The measure of experimental effect could be calculated either by use of S_E or S_C or some combination of the two.

Basis of Standardization	Δ
a) s_E	1.00
b) s_C	0.20
c) $(s_E + s_C)/2$	0.33

The average standard deviation, (c), probably should be eliminated as a mere mindless statistical reaction to a perplexing choice. But both the remaining 1.00 and 0.20 are *correct;* neither can be ruled out as false. It is true, in fact, that the experimental group mean is one standard deviation above the control group mean in terms of the experimental group standard deviation; and, assuming normality, the average subject in the control group is superior to only 16 percent of the members of the experimental group. However, the control group mean is only one-fifth standard deviation below the mean of the experimental group when measured in control group standard deviations; thus, the average experimental group subject exceeds 58 percent of the subjects in the control group. These facts are not contradictory; they are two distinct features of a finding which cannot be expressed by one number. In a meta-analysis of psychotherapy experiments, the problem of heterogeneous standard deviations was resolved from a quite different direction. Suppose that methods A, B, and Control are compared in a single experiment, with the following results:

	Method A	*Method B*	*Control*
Means	50	50	48
Standard Deviations	10	1	4

If effect sizes are calculated using the standard deviations of the "method," then $\triangle_A$ equals 0.20 and $\triangle_B$ equals 2.00—a misleading difference, considering the equality of the method means on the dependent variable. Standardization of mean differences by the control group standard deviation at least has the advantage of allotting equal effect sizes to equal means. This seems reason enough to resolve the choice in favor of the control group standard deviation, at least when there are more than one treatment condition and only one control condition.

In many studies where the emphasis in reporting is on inferential statistics, only pooled information is available about the within-group variances. Since the statistical tests used in these cases depend on an assumption of homogeneity of within-group variances, the test statistics frequently obscure whatever differences in variance might have existed.

When the results of an experiment are expressed as a t-statistic which is reported along with n_1 and n_2 but without means and variances, one can calculate an effect-size, $\triangle$, via the formula

$$\triangle_p = t(1/n_1 + 1/n_2)^{1/2}. \qquad (4)$$

The subscript p indicates that $\triangle$ is based on a pooling of variances. Suppose, to the contrary, that the sample variances are unequal, and that one wishes $\triangle_C$, the mean difference standardized by the control group (group 1, for example) standard deviation. Assuming $n_1 = n_2$, the ratio of $\triangle_C$ to $\triangle_p$ can be derived:

$$\frac{\triangle_C}{\triangle_p} = \left[\left(1 + \frac{s_2^2}{s_1^2}\right) \div 2\right]^{1/2} \qquad (5)$$

As can be seen in Formula (5), $\triangle_C$ is exactly equal to $\triangle_p$ when variances are equal. The bias in the approximation is negative and no greater than about 25 percent when control group variance is less than experimental group variance; however, the bias can grow beyond any bounds when the inequality in the variances is reversed. Hence, the approximation of $\triangle_C$ via backwards solution of a t-statistic (or an F-ratio, as well) could be unsafe if the sample variance of the of the experimental group substantially exceeds that for the control group.

(b) Finding a Standardizing Variance for Studies Without Control Groups. Among the research reports relevant for a particular meta-analysis may be some which provide experimental comparisons of two treatment conditions of interest (say A and B) but include no control condition C. Such studies will provide, at best, standard deviations for the two treatment conditions but neither of these is appropriate for reasons discussed in the previous section. An estimate can be obtained, however. If all studies in which A is compared with C are taken, the observed control group standard deviations can be regressed on the observed treatment A group standard deviations to give:

$$\hat{s}_C = b_0 + b_1 s_A. \tag{6}$$

A similar regression can be established for s_C and s_B from those studies comparing treatment B with control C. Non-linear regressions are possible, of course. From a study comparing only treatments A and B, the observed standard deviations s_A and s_B can be substituted into their separate regression equations to provide two estimates of s_C. These two estimates could be pooled to provide the standard deviation with which to scale the mean difference $(\bar{y}_A - \bar{y}_B)$. From information from other studies about effect sizes for A and B against control, this effect between two treatment conditions could then be converted to separate effects between treatment and control (see "Estimation of Effects from Experiments Involving Many Different Comparisons" in this chapter).

(c) Selecting a Standardizing Variance in Factorial Experimental Designs. The description of experimental findings can become complex. The size of within-group variance is affected by the homogeneity of the experimental subjects and the number of classificatory factors in the design, among other things. Suppose an investigator compares Initial Teaching Alphabet and Traditional methods of reading instruction and reports findings in a two-factor analysis of variance design, Method X Intelligence. What is the proper standard deviation to use in calculating the effect size: the standard deviation within cells of the factorial design, or the standard deviation within methods but crossing intelligence levels? The difference between the effect-size measures calculated by the two methods would probably be substantial. If some attempt is not made to deal with this problem, a source of inexplicable and annoying variance will be left in a group of effect-size measures.

Many experimental comparisons of a treatment and a control condition use more complex designs than the simple comparison of two groups. Some introduce other factors into a higher-order analysis of variance design to examine interactions. In the process these designs create a new definition of within-cell variance. Others introduce stratification of subjects (matching pairs being an extreme example) to reduce the error variance and obtain a more powerful significance test. The use of repeated measures designs in which subjects are matched with themselves is intended to achieve even more power by the same means.

In reports of studies of this type, only the pooled information in analysis of variance tables is provided. Means must be calculated to retrieve an appropriate estimate of the control group standard deviation.

Additional Factors of Theoretical Interest. If a higher order analysis of variance is used to explore interactions between the treatment and other factors, that information should not be lost but should instead be coded into the meta-analysis. It is just such interactions that meta-analysis may reveal between studies. Any results which reveal such interactions within studies should be preserved in the data for the meta-analysis. For example, a study to compare treatment and control conditions (Factor A) may stratify the sample of subjects into males and females (Factor B) to study the interaction of the treatment with the subject's gender. For an effect size based on the difference between the overall treatment and control means ($\bar{y}_{T..} - \bar{y}_{C..}$) the appropriate standard deviation would be that for the total control group. A pooled estimate of this would be given by:

$$\hat{s}_y = \sqrt{\frac{(SS_B + SS_{AB} + SS_x)}{(df_B + df_{AB} + df_w)}} \tag{7}$$

An effect size for males alone would be based on the mean difference ($\bar{y}_{TM.} - \bar{y}_{CM.}$). The appropriate standard deviation would be the one for the control group males for which a pooled estimate would be given by:

$$\hat{s}_y = \sqrt{MS_w}\ . \tag{8}$$

Stratification on a Continuous Variable Correlated with Outcome. In some studies subjects are stratified on a continuous variable which is correlated with the final status measure. This design allows the within cells sum of squares from the corresponding unstratified design to be partitioned as:

$$SS_{w(A)} = SS_B + SS_{AB} + SS_{w(AB)} \tag{9}$$

as for the case where B is a factor of theoretical interest. Although this design also allows a more powerful test of the treatment effect, there is often no substantive interest in the between levels variation or the treatment by levels interaction. The control group standard deviation should be obtained as the pooled estimate in formula (7).

If the stratification is achieved by matching pairs, there will be no $SS_{w(AB)}$ term. Only the terms SS_B and SS_{AB} will exist to be pooled. Where the matched pairs data are analyzed by a dependent groups *t*-test, the standard error of the mean difference between pairs is:

$$\sigma_{\bar{d}} = \sqrt{\frac{\sigma_T^2 + \sigma_C^2 - 2\rho_{TC}\sigma_T\sigma_C}{n}}, \tag{10}$$

where σ_T and σ_C are the standard deviations of the treatment and control groups, ρ_{TC} is the correlation between pairs and n is the number of pairs. If the standard deviations for experimental and control conditions are assumed to be homogeneous, then (10) becomes:

$$\sigma_{\bar{d}} = \sqrt{\frac{2\sigma_y^2}{n}(1 - \rho_{TC})}. \tag{11}$$

If the standard error of the mean difference between pairs is reported, the control group standard deviation on the final status measure can be estimated as:

$$s_y = s_{\bar{d}} \sqrt{\frac{n}{2(1 - r_{TC})}} \tag{12}$$

Since the correlation between pairs, r_{TC}, will probably not be reported, it must be estimated. The matching will have been done on some variable X measured before the experiment. The partial correlation of scores on the outcome measure Y between members of pairs, controlling for the common X score for members of each pair, will be:

$$\rho_{Y_TY_C \cdot X} = \frac{\rho_{Y_TY_C} - \rho_{Y_TX}\rho_{Y_CX}}{\sqrt{(1 - \rho_{Y_TX}^2)(1 - \rho_{Y_CX}^2)}} \tag{13}$$

If the correlation between X and Y is the same for each group, that is ρ_{XY}, then:

$$\rho_{TC \cdot X} = \frac{\rho_{TC} - \rho_{XY}^2}{(1 - \rho_{XY}^2)} \tag{14}$$

and, therefore,

$$\rho_{TC} = \rho_{XY}^2 + (1 - \rho_{XY}^2)\rho_{TC \cdot X} \tag{15}$$

If all that members of a pair have in common can be accounted for by their common scores on the matching variable, then the partial correlation between their scores on any other variable, partialing out their scores on the matching variable, should be zero. A reasonable estimate of the correlation between pairs on the final status measure then would be:

$$\hat{r}_{TC} = r_{XY}^2. \tag{16}$$

If r_{XY} (within group) is not provided in the report, a reasonable guess can be made if something is known about the test involved.

Covariance-Adjusted Final Status Scores. One effect of covariance adjustments is to reduce the within-group standard deviation. If only the covariance-adjusted pooled within-group mean squares, MS_w', is known, a pooled estimate of the within-group standard deviation on final status scores can be obtained from:

$$\hat{s}_{y_2} = \sqrt{\frac{MS'_w}{(1 - r^2_{\hat{y}_1 y_2})} \cdot \frac{(df_w - 1)}{(df_w - 2)}} \tag{17}$$

Approximating △ When the Dependent Variable Is Measured Dichotomously

Experimental outcomes are frequently measured in crude dichotomies where refined metric scales do not exist: dropped out versus persisted in school, remained sober versus resumed drinking, convicted versus not convicted of a crime. It seems inappropriate with such data to calculate means and standard deviations and take a conventional ratio, at least when the mean deviates too greatly from .5. One approach to this problem is to attempt to recover underlying metric information. Suppose that with respect to some underlying but unobservable metric (such as motivation to stay in school) the experimental and control groups are distributed normally. It is assumed that there exists a cut-off point, C_y, such that if motivation to stay in school falls below C_y, the pupil will drop out. What can be observed are the proportions p_e and p_c of the groups which fall below C_y. Under the normal distribution assumption,

$$p_e = \int_{-\infty}^{z_e} \frac{1}{\sqrt{2\pi}} e^{-z^2/2} dz \qquad \text{where} \qquad z_e = \frac{y - \bar{y}_E}{s_E}$$

Clearly, z_e is simply the standard normal deviate which divides the curve at the $100p_e$th percentile and can be obtained from any table of the normal curve. Likewise, z_c is that value of the standard normal variable which cuts off the bottom $100p_c$ percent of the distribution. Since,

$$z_e = \frac{C_y - y_e}{s_e} \qquad \text{and} \qquad z_c = \frac{C_y - \bar{y}_c}{s_c}$$

it can be shown under the assumption of homogeneous variances that

$$z_c - z_e = \frac{\bar{y}_E - \bar{y}_C}{s_y} = \Delta_{E-C}. \tag{18}$$

Thus, effect size measures on hypothetical metric variables can be obtained simply by differencing the standard normal deviates corresponding to the percentages observed in the experimental and control groups. The reasoning followed here is essentially the same as that which underlies *probit analysis* (see Finney, 1971).

Minor technical problems have arisen in connection with the use of transformations of dichotomous data in meta-analysis: (1) what if the two distributions (that giving rise to p_e and that yielding p_c) have different variances?, and (2) how can a probit transformation be carried out when p equals either zero or one?

Heterogeneous Variances. Suppose that one observes p_e as the proportion of cases exceeding some fixed point, C, on a scale of measurement for which Z_e is normally distributed with mean and standard deviation μ_e and σ_e. The quantity p_c is similarly defined with Z_c having mean and standard deviation μ_c and σ_c. Now if p_e and p_c are transformed into the unit normal deviates, z_e and z_c, that cut of the upper $100p_e$ percent and $100p_c$ percent of the normal curve, then:

$$z_e = \frac{C - \mu_E}{\sigma_E} \quad \text{and} \quad z_c = \frac{C - \mu_c}{\sigma_c}. \tag{19}$$

It is easily shown that:

$$z_c - z_e(\sigma_e/\sigma_c) = \frac{\mu_E - \mu_C}{\sigma_c} = \triangle_{E-C}. \tag{20}$$

If one knew the value of σ_e/σ_c or had a good hunch about it, then $\triangle_{E-S}$ could be easily calculated by weighting z_e by the ratio σ_e/σ_c. But it is more realistic (because σ_e/σ_c will nearly always be unknown) to ask how $\triangle_{E-C}$ is affected if σ_e and σ_c are unknown and heterogeneous. Beginning with $z_c - z_e$ and permitting σ_e and σ_c to differ, one quickly arrives at the expression:

$$z_c - z_e = \frac{C(\sigma_e - \sigma_c)}{\sigma_e\sigma_c} + \frac{\sigma_c\mu_e - \sigma_e\mu_c}{\sigma_c\sigma_e}. \tag{21}$$

Heterogeneous variances affect the probit transformation both through their effect on the mean difference and the value of the criterion score. One is advised to be alert to the possibility of unequal variances and to use a transformation such as $z_c - z_e(\sigma_e/\sigma_c)$ when possible.

Probits at the Extremes. A vexing problem with probit transformations from dichotomous to metric data arises when n cases reveal either 0 or n "successes." The proportion $p = f/n$ equals either 0 or 1, and the corresponding unit normal deviates are infinite ($-\infty$ and $+\infty$). Suppose ten experimental subjects are treated for dyslexia, and at the end of six months each reads sufficiently well to be promoted ($p_e = 10/10 = 1$). None of the ten subjects in the control group is promoted ($p_c = 0/10 = 0$). The corresponding unit normal deviates are $z_e = +\infty$ and $z_c = -\infty$, and $\triangle = \infty - (-\infty) = 2\infty$! Suppose that it was decided arbitrarily to change one case in each sample to avoid this problem. Then p_e would be taken equal to 9/10 and p_c to 1/10, giving normal deviates of 1.282 and -1.282, respectively; and $\triangle = 2.564$. Suppose a compromise between 0 and 1 "success" was struck at 0.5 so that p_c equaled $0.5/10 = .05$ and, similarly, $p_e = .95$. The resulting value of Δ is $1.645 - (-1.645) = 3.290$. The differences among 3.290, 2.564, and ∞ are too large to ignore. A method is needed for dealing non-arbitrarily with *p*s of 1 or 0.

If y is binomially distributed with parameters π and n, then $p = y/n$. Assuming a uniform prior distribution of π, the Bayesian posterior distribution of π given y is the ratio of a binomial distribution in π to a beta-distribution in y (Glass, Smith, and Barton, 1979, p. 46). The mean of the posterior, which can be taken to be the Bayesian estimate of π, is $(y + 1)/(n + 2)$. If $y = 0$ in a binomial sample of n, then the Bayesian estimate $\hat{\pi}$ equals $(0 + 1)/(n + 2)$. Likewise, at the other end of the scale, a p of 1 corresponds to a $\hat{\pi}$ of $(n + 1)/(n + 2)$. For example, in the illustration discussed earlier, $p_e = 10/10$ would yield $\hat{\pi}_e = 11/12 = .92$; and $p_c = 0/10$ would give $\hat{\pi}_c = 1/12 = .08$. Hence, Δ equals $1.40 - (-1.40) = 2.80$. This solution seems non-arbitrary and reasonable. Having found it, we see no reason why it should not be applied across the board; that is, regardless of the value of $p = y/n$, if a uniform prior distribution of π is reasonable, then $\hat{\pi}$ should be taken to equal $\hat{\pi} = (y + 1)/(n + 2)$.

Estimation of Effects from Experiments Involving Many Different Comparisons

Collections of experiments often present odd arrays of comparisons to one who wishes an integrated summary of effects. The experimental literature on drugs and psychotherapy addressed the estimation of the separate and interactive effects of drugs and psychotherapy in a variety of ways. Several types of experiment can be identified which inform one about the drug effect alone, or the drug plus the interaction effect, or the psychotherapy plus the drug plus the interaction effect, and so on in various combinations. An experiment that compares patients' progress on drugs with a group of patients receiving a placebo or nothing estimates the simple drug effect; whereas an experiment that compares two groups of patients, one of which receives drugs-plus-psychotherapy and the other of which receives only drugs, provides an estimate of the psychotherapy plus the interaction effect. Denote the drug effect in isolation when compared with a placebo or no treatment by δ; denote the separate psychotherapy effect by ψ; and denote the interaction effect of the two by η. Then the comparison of drug therapy and placebo in an experiment estimates δ. The comparison of drug-plus-psychotherapy with psychotherapy estimates $\delta + \eta$ because both sides of the comparison have equal psychotherapy effects. In Table 1 appear the possible experimental comparisons of drug and psychotherapy and what effects these comparisons estimate. By arranging and averaging the results from experiments of the six different types specified in Table 1, the separate and interactive effects of drug and psychotherapy can be estimated. The organization of data and unknown parameters in the left half of Table 1 can be viewed as a system of six sources of information and three

Table 1. Parametric Structure of Experiments and Average Effects for Studies Comparing Drugs and Psychotherapy

Treatments Compared	*Parameters Estimated*	*Average* Δ	*No. of* Δs
a) Psychotherapy vs. Control	ψ	.30	55
b) Drug therapy vs. Control	δ	.51	351
c) Drug vs. Psychotherapy	$\delta - \psi$	.10	7
d) Drug and Psychotherapy vs. Drug	$\psi + \eta$	.41	10
e) Drug and Psychotherapy vs. Psychotherapy	$\delta + \eta$	.44	94
f) Drug and Psychotherapy vs. Control	$\psi + \delta + \eta$	.65	49

unknown parameters. Least-squares estimates of the parameters can be calculated by ordinary methods.

The question of the main and interactive effects of psychotherapy and drug therapy was addressed in Smith, Glass, and Miller (1980). A total of 112 studies was collected, each of which addressed the question in part with one or more experimental comparisons. These 112 studies yielded 566 Δ effect-size measures. For example, a study in which drug treatment was compared with combined drug and psychotherapy treatment, a standardized mean difference of the following form would result: $\Delta_{D+P-D} = (\bar{y}_{D+P} - \bar{y}_D)/s_y$. In the right half of Table 1 appear the actual average effect sizes calculated from the findings of the 112 experiments.

From simple inspection, it appears that the drug effect of .51 is more than half again as large as the psychotherapy effect of .30. The interaction effect is slightly more difficult to comprehend from merely inspecting the entries in Table 1. That the drug-plus-psychotherapy versus drug comparison, which estimates $\psi + \eta$, is a full one-tenth standard deviation larger than the .30 estimate of ψ from the first line of the table might lead one to believe that η is positive; but the comparison of the estimates of $\delta + \eta$ and δ (being .44 and .51 respectively) reverses this impression. Inspection is too arbitrary and confusing. Several comparisons in the table contain information about the same parameters; it seems reasonable that every source of information about a parameter should be used in estimating it. A complete and standard method of combining the data in Table 1 into estimates of the parameters is needed. Such a method is suggested when one recognizes that the two middle columns of Table 1 constitute a system of linear equations, three of them independent and containing three unknowns (ψ, δ, and η). The method of least-squares statistical estimation can be applied to obtain estimates of the separate and interactive effects of drug and psychotherapy:

$\hat{\psi}$, the separate effect of psychotherapy : .31

$\hat{\delta}$, the separate effect of drug therapy : .42

$\hat{\eta}$, the interactive effect of drug-plus-psychotherapy : .02

Integrating Effects Based on Quantitative Independent Variables

Some types of research study have both dependent, Y, and independent, X variables that can be quantitatively measured, for example, amount of reinforcement (independent) and time-to-criterion (dependent), engaged study time (independent) and learning (dependent), or class size (independent) and achievement (dependent). One desires a technique for integrating many separate studies into an aggregate description of the relationship between the two quantitative variables. The search for such a technique encounters two complications: (1) the values of the independent variables observed in a study may be quite different, and (2) the scales of measurement (mean and variance) of the dependent variables may be quite different as well.

The second complication can be resolved readily. The dependent variable difference in the study between independent variable values X_1 and X_2 can be standardized via

$$\Delta_{X_1 - X_2} = \frac{\bar{y}_1 - \bar{y}_2}{\sigma_y}, \tag{22}$$

where σ_y is an assumed homogeneous within-group standard deviation.

However, the first complication is more problematic. That no two studies need include the same values of X_1 and X_2 makes the representation of the X and Y relationship very complex. This is so in part because Δ is a differential, not a measure on a scale with a non-arbitrary zero point.

One solution to the problem of depicting the X and Y relationship is to regress Δ onto X_1 and X_2 in a three-dimensional space. (An extension of this approach was used by Glass and Smith, 1979, in their study on class size and achievement.) The major drawback of this solution is that the relationship among two variables has been complicated by expression as a relationship among three variables; thus it is inaccessible to many who can comprehend a simple graph but not a complex one. Moreover, in reducing the three dimensional relationship to two dimensions by imposing restrictions (Glass and Smith, 1979), the mathematics grows complicated and attendant problems of statistical inference are obscured. A simpler solution is desirable, and one has been found.

A Logarithmic Model. Consider an illustration from research on class size and achievement. Fourteen experiments were found in which pupils were randomly assigned to classes of different sizes. These fourteen studies yielded over 100 separate comparisons of achievement in smaller and larger classes. The multiplicity of findings is due partly to the fact that in one study there may exist several pairs of class sizes and partly to the fact that a single pair of class sizes may have been measured on more than one achievement test. The latter multiplicity was averaged out and the former retained in the summary of thirty data points in Table 2.

Table 2. Data on the Relationship of Class Size and Achievement from Studies Using Random Assignment of Pupils

Study Number	*Size of Smaller Class*	*Size of Larger Class*	Δ_{S-L}
1.	1	25	.32
2.	1	3	.22
2.	1	25	1.52
2.	3	25	1.22
3.	17	35	−.29
4.	28	112	−.03
5.	1	2	.36
5.	1	5	.52
5.	1	23	.83
5.	2	5	.22
5.	2	23	.57
5.	5	23	.31
6.	15	30	.17
7.	16	23	.05
7.	16	30	.04
7.	16	37	.08
7.	23	30	.04
7.	23	37	.04
7.	30	37	0
8.	20	28	.15
9.	26	50	.29
10.	1	32	.65
11.	15	37	.40
11.	15	60	1.25
11.	37	60	.65
12.	1	8	.30
13.	15	45	.07
14.	1	14	.72
14.	1	30	.78
14.	14	30	.17

$$\Delta_{S-L} = \frac{\bar{y}_S - \bar{y}_L}{(s_S + s_L)/2}$$

n = 14 studies
N = 30 comparisons

One might expect class size and achievement to be related in something of an experimental or geometric fashion—reasoning that one pupil with one teacher learns some amount, two pupils learn less, three pupils learn still less, and so on. Furthermore, the drop in learning from one to two pupils could be expected to be larger than the drop from two to three, which in turn is probably larger than the drop from three to four, and so on. A logarithmic curve represents one such relationship:

$$y = \beta - \beta \log_e C + \epsilon, \qquad (23)$$

where C denotes class size.

In formula (23), α represents the achievement for a "class" of one person, since $\log_e 1 = 0$, and β represents the speed of decrease in achievement as a class size increases.

Formula (23) cannot be fitted to data directly because Y is not measured on a common scale across studies. This problem can be circumvented by calculating Δ_{S-L} for each comparison of a smaller and a larger class size within a study. Then, from formulas (22) and (23) one has

$$\begin{aligned} \Delta_{S-L} &= (\alpha - \beta \log_e S + \epsilon_1) - (\alpha - \beta \log_e L + \epsilon_2) \\ &= \beta(\log_e L - \log_e S) + \epsilon_1 - \epsilon_2 \qquad (24) \\ &= \beta \log_e (L/S) + \epsilon . \end{aligned}$$

The model in formula (24) is particularly simple and straightforward. The values of Δ_{S-L} are merely regressed onto the logarithm of the ratio of the larger to the smaller class size, forcing the least-squares regression through the origin.

$$\hat{\beta} = \frac{\Sigma(\Delta_{S-L})(\log_e L/S)}{\Sigma(\log_e L/S)^2}. \qquad (25)$$

The estimate of β for the data in Table 2 equals 0.27. The value of r is .64. The resulting curve relating class size C to achievement in standard-score units appears as Figure 1.

Non-Parametric Integration When the Independent Variable Is Quantitative

The methods of the previous section assume a model for the relationship between the dependent and a quantitative independent variable. Standardized contrasts of the form $\Delta_{X_1 - X_2}$ are used to estimate the parameters of the model. In many instances, too little will be known about the relationship to hypothesize even an approximate model. Then, perhaps, an approach modeled after Tukey's methods of exploratory data analysis might be more appropriate (Tukey, 1977). No functional relationship need be hypothesized, and the data themselves will determine the shape of the curve. An example will help clarify the approach, which may differ in details in particular applications.

Andrews, Guitar, and Howie (in press) performed a meta-analysis of experimental studies of stuttering therapies. Effect sizes were calculated for forty-two studies; all studies were pretest versus post-test designs without control groups. Effects were assessed by comparing the post-test mean against the pretest mean and standardizing by the pretest standard deviation.

Figure 1. Data in Table 2 Fitted to the Log Model of Formula (24)

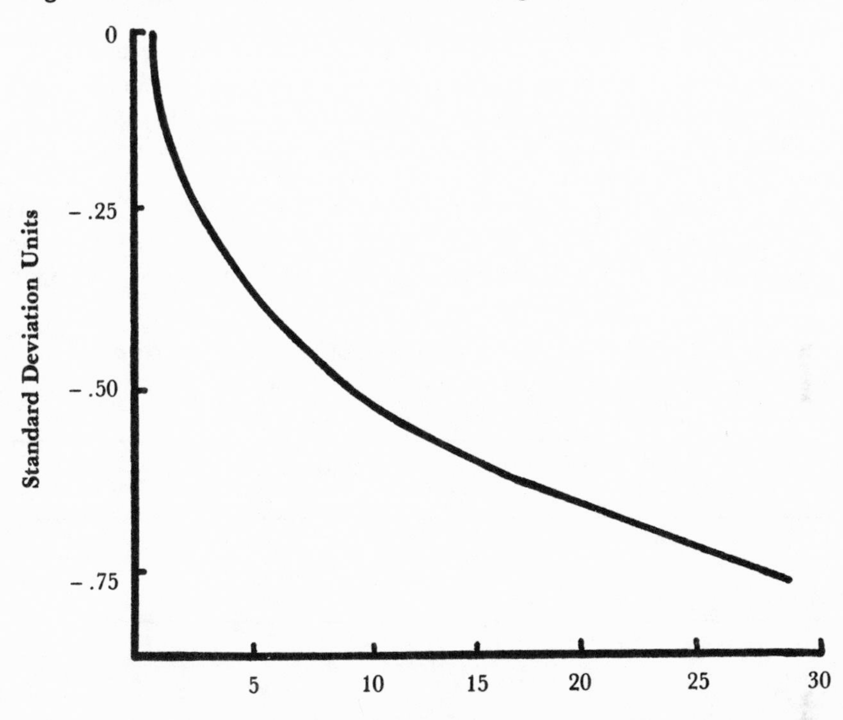

The forty-two studies yielded 116 Δs. These Δs were categorized by the type of therapy applied, the duration of the therapy, type of outcome measure, and several other features of the therapy and the clients. Differences in average effect were obtained across types of therapy: Prolonged Speech therapy gave a $\overline{\Delta}_{E-C} = 1.65$ for 47 effects; at the other end of the scale, Systematic Desensitization gave a $\overline{\Delta}_{E-C} = 0.54$ for 5 effects (Andrews, Guitar, and Howie, in press, Table 3). No correlation was found between the number of months after therapy at which effects were measured and the size of effect.

This lack of correlation seemed surprising and prompted the further search for a decay of effect across time. The "follow-up time" variable and type of therapy are confounded in the Andrews stuttering data set. For example, Airflow therapy showed an average Δ of 0.92, but these outcomes were measured at 4.2 months after therapy on the average. On the other hand, Attitude therapy showed a $\overline{\Delta} = 0.85$ for an average follow-up time of 3.3 months. The only real difference between Attitude and Airflow average effects might be attributable to varying follow-up times for measurement of benefits. Likewise, the effect of different follow-up times may reflect therapy differences. For this reason, the pattern of decay in effects across time should be examined separately within each type of therapy. But another feature of the studies is also confounded with follow-up time and should be likewise controlled. Therapies differed with respect to the attention given to providing for post-therapy maintenance of the gains made during therapy. Andrews and his colleagues classified each study by whether there were *many, some* or *no* provisions made for maintenance of gains achieved during therapy. It seemed sensible to cross-classify effects by therapy type and maintenance provisions before examining the data for the decay of treatment phenomenon. Thus, 107 of the 116 effect sizes were cross-classified into the cells of an 8 × 3 (therapy type × maintenance provision) table, and the cell entries were averaged.

The averaging of effects resulted in an 8 × 3 table (see Table 3). The typical entry is a triplet of numbers of the form (a, b, c), where *a* is the follow-up time in months, *b* is the average $\bar{\Delta}_{0-a}$, and *c* is the number of values aver-

Table 3. Follow-Up Time, Average Effect Size, and Number of Effects Averaged Classified by Type of Therapy and Provisions for Maintenance

		Maintenance Provisions	
Therapy Type	*1: None*	*2: Some*	*3: Many*
Airflow		1, .88, 1 3, .74, 1 16, .86, 1	
Rhythm	0, .66, 1 14, .76, 2		0, 1.26, 7 6, 1.57, 2 9, 1.60, 10 12, .86, 4
Shadow	0, .17, 1 14, .38, 1		
Gentle Onset	0, 1.12, 2 1, 1.38, 1 10, 1.12, 1 25. 1.15, 1		0, 2.37, 2 10, 1.52, 2
Biofeedback			0, .88, 2 12, 1.03, 2
Attitude	0, .71, 7 9, 1.11, 4		
Prolonged Speech	0, 2.02, 6 3, 2.42, 2 6, 1.27, 2 9, 2.17, 3 11, 1.77, 1		0, 1.62, 9 2, 2.02, 3 12, 1.16, 8 15, 1.16, 8 18, 1.36, 3
Desensitization	0, .69, 1 1, .89, 1 20, 1.07, 1	1, .01, 1 3, .03, 1	

aged. (The symbol $\triangle_{0-a}$ denotes the standardized mean difference, $\triangle$, between time 0 [pretest] and time *a* [follow-up test] in months.) Within a cell of Table 3, the entries were graphed in a connected line. Consider, for example, the cell for Rhythm therapy with many provisions for maintenance. The four data points can be graphed, as shown by the solid line in Figure 2. The broken line represents the three data points from Airflow therapy at the second maintenance level. The elevation of either line on the graph is immaterial; only the slope of the line relative to the abscissa is significant. The number in parentheses beside each line is the average of the number of effects, $\triangle_{0-a}$, that exist at each end of the line; for example, the first segment of the solid line is

Figure 2. Graphs of Effects Over Time for Two Cells of Table 3

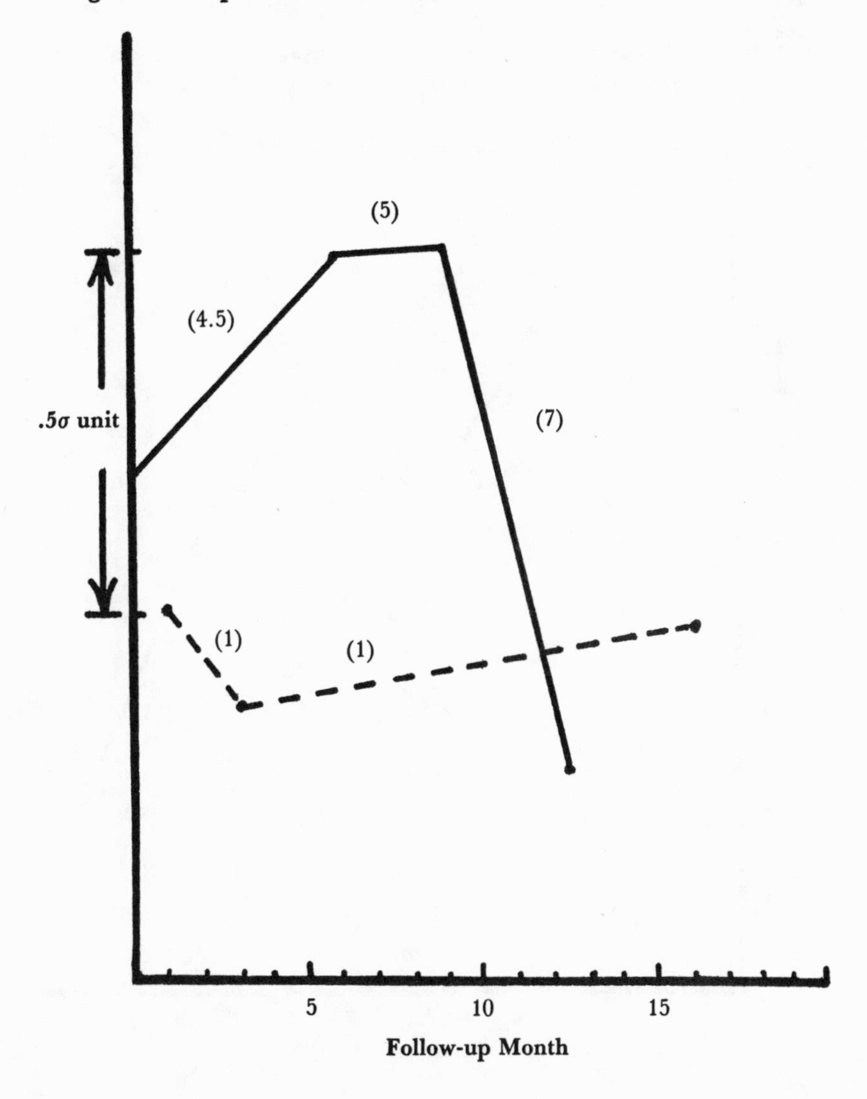

based on seven Δs at zero months and two Δs at six months—hence the weight $(7+2)/2 = 4.5$ for the line segment.

One approach to aggregating the data on slopes is to take a weighted average of all the lines above two successive months. For example, the slope of the solid line in Figure 2 between months 1 and 2 is $+.05 = \frac{1.57 - 1.26}{6 \text{ mos.}}$; the slope of the broken line is $-.07$. Since the weight for the solid line segment is 4.5 and for the dashed line, 1.0, the weighted average slope between months 1 and 2 is $[4.5(.05) + 1.0(-.07)]/(4.5 + 1.0) = -.028$.

If the above procedure were repeated for each successive pair of months and for all twelve lines that can be drawn from the data in Table 3, a complete aggregate is obtained. Such a curve is depicted in Figure 3. The curve shows a loss of benefits over the first twelve months after termination of therapy; the

Figure 3. Aggregation by Weighted Averaging of Data in Table 3 on the Decay of Stuttering Therapy Effects

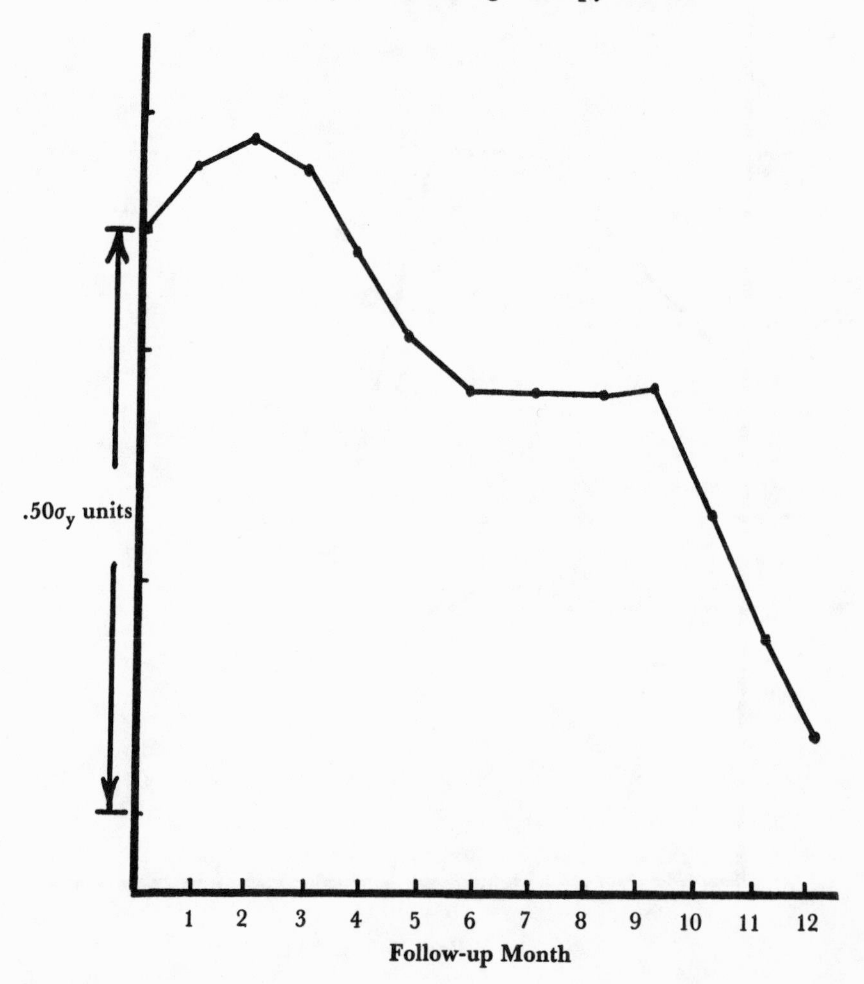

average loss is roughly one-half standard deviation. Although the general trend in the curve is unmistakably downward, not every intermediate twist and curve is to be taken seriously as a stable, replicable feature of the true relationship. Even though approximately twenty Δs are still determining the slope of the aggregate curve in Figure 3 at twelve months post therapy, the estimates of the points on the curve are probably subject to a fairly large sampling error. Inferential techniques, perhaps drawing on Tukey's jackknife procedure (Mosteller and Tukey, 1968), would illuminate the question of the reliability of the determination of the curve.

References

Andrews, G., Guitar, B., and Howie, P. "A Meta-Analysis of Stuttering Therapy Outcome Studies." *Journal of Speech and Hearing Disorders,* in press.

Cronbach, L. J., and Furby, L. "How We Should Measure 'Change'—or Should We?" *Psychological Bulletin,* 1970, *74,* 68–80.

Finney, D. J. *Probit Analysis.* (3rd ed.). Cambridge: Cambridge University Press, 1971.

Glass, G. V. "Integrating Findings: The Meta-Analysis of Research." *Review of Research in Education,* 1977, *5,* 351–379.

Glass, G. V, and Smith, M. L. "Meta-Analysis of Research on the Relationship of Class Size and Achievement." *Educational Evaluation and Policy Analysis,* 1979, *1,* 2–16.

Glass, G. V, Smith, M. L., and Barton, M. A. "Methods of Integrative Analysis." Annual Report of Grant No. NIE–G–78–0148 to the National Institute of Education. Boulder: Laboratory of Educational Research, University of Colorado: August 1979.

Hedges, L. V. "Combining the Results of Experiments Using Different Scales of Measurement." Unpublished paper. Stanford, Calif.: School of Education, Stanford University, 1979.

McGaw, B., and Glass, G. V. "Choice of the Metric for Effect Size." *American Educational Research Journal,* in press.

Mosteller, F. M., and Tukey, J. W. "Data Analysis, Including Statistics." In G. Lindzey and E. Aronson (Eds.), *Handbook of Social Psychology.* (2nd ed.) Reading, Mass.: Addison-Wesley, 1968.

Smith, M. L., Glass, G. V, and Miller, T. I. *Benefits of Psychotherapy.* Baltimore: Johns Hopkins University Press, 1980.

Gene V Glass is professor of education at the University of Colorado. He has been president of the American Educational Research Association, editor of the Review of Educational Research, *and associate editor for methodology of the* Psychological Bulletin.

Each of several methods for combining significance effects has its advantages and limitations.

Summarizing Significance Levels

Robert Rosenthal

Since the 1930s there has been a slow but steady increase in the literature that addresses the question of how to obtain an overall level of significance for the results of runs of studies (see Bhattacharya, 1961; Birnbaum, 1954; Fisher, 1938, 1948; Good, 1955, 1958; Lancaster, 1949; Naylor, 1967; Nelson, 1966; Oosterhoff, 1969; E. S. Pearson, 1938, 1950; K. Pearson, 1933; Quenouille, 1953; Radhakrishna, 1965; Rao, 1953; Wallis, 1942; Yates, 1955). The purpose of this chapter is to summarize briefly and make readily available for wider use the major methods for combining the probabilities obtained from two or more studies testing essentially the same directional hypothesis. While it is possible to do so, no consideration is given here to questions of combining results from studies in which the direction of the results cannot be made immediately apparent, as would be the case for F tests (employed in analysis of variance) with $df > 1$ for the numerator or for chi-square tests (of independence in contingency tables) with $df > 1$. Although this discussion is intended to be self-contained, it is not intended to serve as a summary of all the useful ideas on this topic that are contained in the literature referenced. The seminal work of Mosteller and Bush (1954) is especially recommended.

Preparation of this chapter was supported in part by the National Science Foundation. It is based in part on the article, "Combining Results of Independent Studies," *Psychological Bulletin,* 1978, *85,* 185-193.

Preliminary Considerations

Significance Levels and Effect Sizes. Although the focus of this chapter is on summarizing significance levels it should be emphasized that almost always when we summarize significance levels we should also summarize the magnitudes of the effects obtained in the studies summarized. Perhaps the fullest general discussion of effect size estimation is that by Cohen (1969; 1977). In this volume, Glass employs creatively a variant of one of Cohen's effect size estimators (*d*). It will aid us in our thinking about effect sizes and significance levels if we keep in mind the very general relationship:

$$\text{Significance Test} = \text{Effect Size} \times \text{Size of Study}$$

Thus, for any effect size that is nonzero the degree of statistical significance is monotonically related to the number of sampling units employed in our study. We may illustrate this relationship in the case of χ^2 (for $df = 1$) by noting that $\chi^2 = \phi^2 \times N$ where ϕ is the product moment correlation applied to variables that are dichotomous. In the case of t (with equal sample sizes) $t = d/2 \times \sqrt{df}$ where d is the difference between group means divided by the common within group standard deviation.

These relationships show that one might be dealing with very significant results that are very small or very large in magnitude, or with not at all significant results that are also very small or very large in magnitude. To compute statistical significance, then, we must know both the size of the effect and the sample size; to compute the size of the effect we must know both the results of the test of significance and the sample size.

As a practical matter it should be noted that we can often estimate the size of an experimental effect from just the level of significance of the experimental result. This is due to the fact that, for given research areas, there tend to be limited ranges of sample sizes so that N or *df* can be estimated. A recent analysis by Rosenthal and Rubin (1978) found for eight areas of research on interpersonal expectancy effects that the range of correlations between levels of significance defined by standard normal deviates (Z) and sizes of effects (Cohen's d) was from .46 to .91 with a median correlation of .69. A more recent analysis by DePaulo, Zuckerman, and Rosenthal (1980) found a correlation between d and Z of .84 for 16 studies of the accuracy of decoding cues to deception.

The File Drawer Problem. Both behavioral researchers and statisticians have long suspected that the studies published in the behavioral sciences are a biased sample of the studies that are actually carried out (Bakan, 1967; McNemar, 1960; Smart, 1964; Sterling, 1959). The extreme view of this problem, the "file drawer problem," is that the journals are filled with the 5 percent of the studies that show Type 1 errors, while the file drawers back at the lab are filled with the 95 percent of the studies that show nonsignificant ($p > .05$) results (Rosenthal, 1979).

In the past there was very little we could do to assess the net effect of studies tucked away in file drawers that did not make the magic .05 level (Rosenthal and Gaito, 1963, 1964). Now, however, although no definitive solution to the problem is available, we can establish reasonable boundaries on the problem and estimate the degree of damage to any research conclusion that could be done by the file drawer problem. The fundamental idea in coping with the file drawer problem is simply to calculate the number of studies averaging null results that must be in the file drawers before the overall probability of a Type I error can be just brought to any desired level of significance, say $p = .05$. This number of filed studies, or the tolerance for future null results, is then evaluated for whether such a tolerance level is small enough to threaten the overall conclusion drawn by the reviewer. If the overall level of significance of the research review will be brought down to the level of *just significant* by the addition of just a few more null results, the finding is not resistant to the file drawer threat.

Computation. To find the number (X) of new, filed, or unretrieved studies averaging null results required to bring the new overall p to any desired level, say, just significant at $p = .05$ ($Z = 1.645$), one simply writes:

$$1.645 = k\bar{Z}_k/\sqrt{k + X}\,. \tag{1}$$

where k is the number of studies combined and $\bar{Z}_k$ is the mean Z obtained for the k studies.

Rearrangement shows, then, that

$$X = (k/2.706)[k(\bar{Z}_k)^2 - 2.706]. \tag{2}$$

An alternative formula that may be more convenient when the sum of the Zs (ΣZ) is given rather than the mean Z as follows: $X = [(\Sigma Z)^2/2.706] - k$. One method based on counting rather than adding Zs may be easier to compute and can be employed when exact p levels are not available; but it is probably less powerful. If X is the number of new studies required to bring the overall p to .50 (not to .05), s is the number of summarized studies significant at $p < .05$, and n is the number of summarized studies not significant at .05, then $X = 19s - n$. Another conservative alternative when exact p levels are not available is to set $Z = .00$ for any nonsignificant result and to set $Z = 1.645$ for any result significant at $p < .05$.

Illustration. In 1969, 94 experiments examining the effects of interpersonal self-fulfilling prophecies were summarized (Rosenthal, 1969). The mean Z of these studies was 1.014, k was 94, and Z for the studies combined was $9.83 = 94\,(1.014)/(94)^{1/2}$.

How many new, filed, or unretrieved studies (X) would be required to bring this very large Z down to a barely significant level ($Z = 1.645$)? By Equation 2,

$$X = (94/2.706)[94(1.014)^2 - 2.706] = 3.263,$$

one finds that 3,263 studies averaging null results ($\bar{Z} = .00$) must be crammed into file drawers before one would conclude that the overall results were due to sampling bias in the studies summarized by the reviewer. In a more recent summary of the same area of research (Rosenthal and Rubin, 1978) the mean Z of 345 studies was 1.22, k was 345, and X was 65,123! Thus, over 65,000 unreported studies averaging a null result would have to exist somewhere before the overall results could reasonably be ascribed to sampling bias.

Discussion. There is both a sobering and a cheering lesson to be learned from careful study of Equation 2. The sobering lesson is that small numbers of studies that are not very significant, even when their combined p is significant, may well be misleading in that only a few studies filed away could change the combined significant result to a nonsignificant one. The cheering lesson is that when the number of studies available grows large or the mean directional Z grows large, the file drawer hypothesis as a plausible rival hypothesis can be safely ruled out.

At the present time no firm guidelines can be given as to what constitutes an unlikely number of unretrieved or unpublished studies. For some areas of research 100 or even 500 unpublished and unretrieved studies may be a plausible state of affairs, whereas for others even 10 or 20 seems unlikely. Probably any rough and ready guide should be based partly on k so that as more studies are known it becomes more plausible that other studies in that area may be in those file drawers. Perhaps one could regard as resistant to the file drawer problem any combined results for which the tolerance level (X) reaches $5k + 10$. This seems a conservative but reasonable tolerance level; the $5k$ portion suggests that it is unlikely that the file drawers have more than five times as many studies as the reviewer, and the 10 sets the minimum number of studies that could be filed away at 15 (when $k = 1$).

It appears that more and more reviewers of research literature are estimating average effect sizes and combined ps of the studies they summarize. It would be very helpful to readers if, for each combined p they presented, reviewers also gave the tolerance for future null results associated with their overall significance level.

Comparing Significance Levels. Before combining either the size of the effects or the significance levels of a set of studies, it is often useful first to examine the homogeneity of the set of results. A standard procedure for testing the homogeneity of a set of effect sizes is given by Snedecor and Cochran (1967, p. 187). In this procedure, effect sizes in the form of rs are examined by converting each r into its Fisher Z equivalent and computing:

$$\Sigma[(n_i - 3)\,(Z_i - \bar{Z}_w)^2] = \chi^2(K - 1)$$

where n_i is the number of sampling units upon which each r is based, Z_i is the Fisher Z equivalent of each r as found in the appropriate table of any statistics text, and $\bar{Z}_w$ is the mean of the K Zs each having been weighted by $n_i - 3$. The resulting quantity is distributed as χ^2 with $(K - 1)$ *df*.

An analogous procedure can be employed to test for the homogeneity of significance levels (Rosenthal and Rubin, 1979). Each of the K p levels being summarized is converted to its standard normal deviate (Z) and the sum of the squares of the deviations of the K Zs about the mean Z is computed, a quantity also distributed as χ^2 with $(K-1)$ *df*.

$$\Sigma(Z_i - \bar{Z})^2 = \chi^2(K-1)$$

Combining Probabilities

The Basic Methods. Table 1 presents a set of results of five fictional studies. The first column of information about the studies lists the results of the t test. The sign preceding t gives the direction of the results; a plus sign means the difference is consistent with the bulk of the results, a negative sign means the difference is not consistent. The second column records the *df* upon which each t was based. The third column gives the one-tailed p associated with each t. It should be noted that one-tail ps are always less than .50 when the results are in the consistent direction but they are always greater than .50 when the results are not consistent. For example, study 3 with a t of $-.60$ is tabulated with a one-tail p of .72. If the t had been in the consistent direction, that is, $+.60$, the one-tail p would have been .28. It is important to note that it is the direction of difference which is found to occur on the average that is assigned the + sign and hence the lower one-tail p. The basic computations and results are identical whether we were very clever and predicted the net direction of effect or not clever at all and got it quite wrong. At the very end of our calculations, we can double the final overall level of significance if we want to make an allowance for not having predicted the net direction of effect.

The fourth column of Table 1 gives the size of the effect defined in terms of a proportion of the σ common to the two samples being compared (Cohen's d, 1969). Not simply in connection with combining ps but at any time that test statistics such as t or F or Z are reported, estimated effect sizes should routinely be reported. The particular effect size d seems to be the most useful one to employ when two groups are being compared. Perhaps the handiest way to compute d is by the formula: $2t/\sqrt{df}$. The fifth column gives the standard normal deviate, or Z associated with each p value. The final column of Table 1 lists the natural logarithms of the one-tail ps of column 3 multiplied by -2. Each is a quantity distributed as χ^2 with 2 *df* and is an ingredient of the first method of combining p levels to be presented (Fisher, 1938).

Adding Logs. The last column of Table 1 is really a list of χ^2 values. Since the sum of independent χ^2s is also distributed as χ^2 with *df* equal to the sum of the *df*s of the χ^2s added, we need only add the five χ^2s of Table 1 and look up this new χ^2 with $5 \times 2 = 10$ *df*. The results are given just below the row of medians of Table 1. $\chi^2 = 22.97$ which is associated with a p of .006, one-tail, when $df = 10$.

The method of adding logs, the Fisher method, though frequently

Table 1. Methods for Combining Probabilities of Independent Experiments

Study	*t*	*df*	*One-tail* *p**	*Effect Size σ*	*Z*	$-2 \log_e p$
1	+1.19	40	.12	.38	+1.17	4.24
2	+2.39	60	.01	.62	+2.33	9.21
3	−0.60	10	.72	−.38	−0.58	0.66
4	+1.52	30	.07	.56	+1.48	5.32
5	+0.98	20	.17	.44	+0.95	3.54
Σ	+5.48	160	1.09	+1.62	+5.35	22.97
Mean	+1.10	32	.22	+.32	+1.07	4.59
Median	+1.19	30	.12	+.44	+1.17	4.24

*Whenever *p*s from different studies are to be combined they should always be given as one-tailed (see text). Sufficiently accurate *p*s can usually be obtained by interpolation or by using extended tables (for example, Federighi, 1959).

Method of Adding Logs

$$\chi^2\ (df = 2N) = \Sigma - 2 \log_e p = 22.97 \qquad p = .006 \text{ one-tail}$$

Method of Adding Probabilities (applicable when Σp near unity or less)

$$P = \frac{(\Sigma p)^N}{N!} = \frac{(1.09)^5}{5!} = .006 \text{ one-tail}$$

Method of Adding ts

$$Z = \frac{\Sigma t}{\sqrt{\Sigma [df/(df-2)]}} = \frac{5.48}{\sqrt{40/38 + 60/58 + 10/8 + 30/28 + 20/18}} = \frac{5.48}{\sqrt{5.5197}} = 2.33 \quad p = .01 \text{ one-tail}$$

Method of Adding Zs

$$Z = \frac{\Sigma Z}{\sqrt{N}} = \frac{5.35}{\sqrt{5}} = 2.39,\ p = .009 \text{ one-tail}$$

Method of Adding Weighted Zs

$$Z = \frac{T}{\sigma_T} = \frac{df_1 Z_1 + df_2 Z_2 + \ldots + df_n Z_n}{\sqrt{df_1^2 + df_2^2 + \ldots + df_n^2}}$$

$$= \frac{(40)(+1.17) + (60)(+2.33) + \ldots + (20)(+0.95)}{\sqrt{(40)^2 + (60)^2 + \ldots + (20)^2}}$$

$$= \frac{244.2}{\sqrt{6600}} = 3.01,\ p = .0013$$

Method of Testing Mean p

$$Z = (.50 - \bar{p})(\sqrt{12N})$$

$$= (.50 - .22)(\sqrt{12(5)}) = 2.17,\ p = .015 \text{ one-tail}$$

Method of Testing Mean Z

$$t = \frac{\Sigma Z/N}{\sqrt{MS_{(Z)}/N}} = \frac{+1.07}{\sqrt{.22513}} = 2.26,\ df = 4,\ p < .05 \text{ one-tail}$$

or

$$F = \frac{(\Sigma Z)^2}{N\ MS_{(Z)}} = 5.09,\ df = 1,4,\ p < .05 \text{ one-tail}$$

cited, suffers from the disadvantage that it can yield results that are inconsistent with such simple overall tests as the sign test. Thus, for a large number of studies, if the vast majority showed results in one direction we could easily reject the null hypothesis by the sign test even if the consistent p values were not very much below .50. However, under these situations the Fisher method would not yield an overall significant p (Mosteller and Bush, 1954). Another problem with the Fisher method is that if two studies with equally and strongly significant results in opposite directions are obtained, the Fisher method supports the significance of either outcome! Thus ps of .001 for A>B and .001 for B>A combine to a $p<.01$ for A>B or B>A (Adcock, 1960). Despite these limitations, the Fisher method remains the best known and most discussed of all the methods of combining independent probabilities (Anderson and Bancroft, 1952; Baker, 1952; van Elteren, 1960; Fisher, 1948; Good, 1958; Gordon, Loveland, and Cureton, 1952; Lancaster, 1967; Littell and Folks, 1971; Pearson, 1938, 1950; Puri, 1965; Wallis, 1942).

Adding Probabilities. A powerful method has been described by Edgington (1972a) in which the combined probability emerges when the sum of the observed p levels is raised to the power equivalent to the number of studies being combined (N) and divided by N!. Essentially, this formula gives the area of a right triangle when the results of two studies are being combined, the volume of a pyramid when the results of three studies are combined, and the n-dimensional generalization of this volume when more studies are involved. Table 1 shows the results to be equivalent to those obtained by the Fisher method for this set of data. The basic Edgington method is useful and ingenious but is limited to small sets of studies since it requires that the sum of the p levels not exceed unity by very much. When the sum of the p levels does exceed unity the overall p obtained tends to be too conservative unless special corrections are introduced.

Adding ts. A method that has none of the disadvantages of the preceding two methods was described by Winer (1971). Based on the result that the variance of the t distribution for any given df is $df/(df-2)$, it requires adding the obtained t values and dividing that sum by the square root of the sum of the dfs associated with the ts after each df has been divided by $df-2$.

The result of the calculation is itself a standard normal deviate that is associated with a particular probability level when each of the ts is based on df of 10 or so. When applied to the data of Table 1 this method yields $p=.01$, one-tail, a result quite close to the earlier two results. The limitation of this method is that it cannot be employed at all when the size of the samples for which t is computed becomes less than three because that would involve dividing by zero or by a negative value. In addition the method may not give such good approximations to the normal with $df<10$ for each t.

Adding Zs. Perhaps the simplest of all, the Stouffer method (Mosteller and Bush, 1954), asks us only to add the standard normal deviates or Zs associated with the ps obtained and divide by the square root of the number of studies being combined (Adcock, 1960; Cochran, 1954; Stouffer, Suchman,

DeVinney, Star, and Williams, 1949, p. 45). Each Z was a standard normal deviate under the null hypothesis, and the variance of the sum of independent normal deviates is the sum of their variances—here, the number of studies since each study has unit variance. Table 1 shows results for the Stouffer method that are very close to those obtained by the method of adding ts ($Z = 2.39$ versus $Z = 2.33$).

Adding Weighted Zs. Mosteller and Bush (1954) have suggested a technique that permits us to weight each standard normal deviate by the size of the sample on which it is based (or by its *df*) or by any other desirable positive weighting such as the elegance, internal validity, or ecological validity of the individual study. The method requires us to add the products of our weights and zs and to divide this sum by the square root of the sum of the squared weights. Table 1 shows the results of the application of the weighted Stouffer method with *df* employed as weights. We note that the result is the lowest overall p we have seen. That is due to the fact that, for the example given, the lowest p levels are given the heaviest weighting because they are associated with the largest sample sizes and *df.* Lancaster (1961) has noted that when weighting is employed the Z method is preferable to weighting applied to the Fisher method for reasons of computational convenience and because the final sum obtained is again a normal variable. Finally, for the very special case of just two studies, Zelen and Joel (1959) describe the choice of weights to minimize Type II errors.

Testing the Mean p. Edgington (1972b) has recently proposed a normal curve method to be used when there are four or more studies to be combined. The mean of the ps to be combined is subtracted from .50 and this quantity is multiplied by the square root of 12N, where N is the number of studies to be combined. (The presence of a 12 derives from the fact that the variance of the population of p values is 1/12.)

Testing the Mean Z. In this modification of the Stouffer method, Mosteller and Bush (1954) first convert p levels to Z values and then compute a t-test on the mean Z value obtained with the *df* for t equal to the number of Z values available minus one. Mosteller and Bush, however, advise against this procedure when there are fewer than five studies to be combined. That suggestion grows out of the low power of the t test when based on few observations. Table 1 illustrates this low power by showing that this method yields the largest combined p of any of the methods reviewed.

Additional Methods.

Counting. When the number of studies to be combined grows large, a number of counting methods can be employed (Brozek and Tiede, 1952; Jones and Fiske, 1953; Wilkinson, 1951). Thus the number of p values below .50 can be called +, the number of p values above .50 can be called −, and a sign test can be performed. Thus, if 12 of 15 results are consistent in either direction the sign test tells us that results so rare "occur by chance" only 3.6 percent of the time. The χ^2 statistic may also be useful in comparing the number of studies expected to reach a given level of significance, under the null hypothesis, with the number actually reaching that level (Rosenthal, 1969,

1976; Rosenthal and Rosnow, 1975). In this two-cell table arrangement, when there are fewer than 100 studies but more than 9 it may be useful to enter in one cell an expected frequency of 5 and in the other an expected frequency of N–5. The observed frequency for the first cell then is the number of studies reaching a $p < \frac{5}{N}$. The observed frequency for the second cell is the number of studies with $p > \frac{5}{N}$. The resulting χ^2 can then be entered into a χ^2 table or the square root of χ^2 can be computed to yield a standard normal deviate, or Z of the kind we have been discussing in this chapter. Although clearcut results on the issue are not available, it appears that the counting methods may not be as powerful as other methods described here.

Blocking. The last method, adapted from the procedure given by Snedecor and Cochran (1967; see also Cochran and Cox, 1957) requires that we reconstruct the means, sample sizes, and mean square within conditions for each of our studies and then combine the data into an overall anova in which studies are regarded as a blocking variable. If required because of differences among the various studies in their means and variances, the dependent variables of the various studies can be put onto a common scale (for example, zero mean and unit variance).

When studies are assumed to be a fixed factor, as they sometimes are (Cochran and Cox, 1957) or when the *MS* for treatments × studies is small relative to the *MS* within, the treatment effect is tested against the pooled *MS* within (Cochran and Cox, 1957). When the studies are regarded as a random factor and when the *MS* for treatments × studies is substantial relative to the *MS* within (say, $F > 2$), the treatments × studies effect is the appropriate error term for the treatment effect. Regardless of whether studies are viewed as fixed or random factors, the main effect of studies and the interaction of treatments × studies are tested against the *MS* within. Substantial main effects of studies may or may not be of much interest but substantial treatments × studies interaction effects will usually be of considerable interest. It will be instructive to study the residuals closely for clues as to the nature of the possible moderating variables affecting the operation of the treatment effect. Analysis of the residuals might show, for example, that it is the better (or more poorly) designed studies that show greater predicted effects. The blocking method is sometimes not applicable because authors have not reported sufficient data in their papers.

Table 2 illustrates this last method as applied to the studies of Table 1. Both a weighted (by n) and an unweighted anova were computed and both results fell within the range of results obtained by our earlier methods (Table 1). The weighted anova (proportional n approach) was substantially more significant because the larger studies showed the larger effects in this particular example. The only real disadvantage of this approach is that it may involve considerably more work than some of the other methods, especially when the number of studies grows from just a few to dozens, scores, or hundreds.

Choosing a Method. Table 3 shows the advantages, limitations, and indications for use of each of the nine methods of combining probabilities. Various methods have special advantages under special circumstances. Thus, if con-

Table 2. The Blocking Method of Combining Probabilities Applied to the Studies of Table 1

Study	*Control Mean (n)*	*Experimental Mean (n)*	*Unweighted Σ*	*Weighted Σ*	*MS Error*
1	0.48 (21)	2.00 (21)	2.48	52.08	17.13
2	0.00 (31)	2.48 (31)	2.48	76.88	16.69
3	2.00 (6)	0.48 (6)	2.48	14.88	19.25
4	0.12 (16)	2.36 (16)	2.48	39.68	17.37
5	0.36 (11)	2.12 (11)	2.48	27.28	17.74
Unweighted Σ	2.96 (5)	9.44 (5)	12.40	—	17.64
Weighted Σ	27.96 (85)	182.84 (85)	—	210.80	17.22[a]

Anova

Unweighted Source	*df*	*MS*	*F*	*Weighted Source*	*df*	*MS*	*F*
Treatments	1	52.51	2.98[c]	Treatments	1	141.10	8.19[d]
Studies	4	0.00[b]	—	Studies	4	0.00[b]	—
Treat × St.	4	16.38	—	Treat × St.	4	10.64	—
Error	160	17.64		Error	160	17.22	—

[a]Based on *df*, not *n*.
[b]In the example constructed here and, more generally, in cases wherein the data from each study are standardized with zero mean and unit variance, the mean square for studies is set at zero.
[c]$z = 1.70$; $p = .045$ one-tail.
[d]$z = 2.81$; $p = .0025$ one-tail.

fronted by 200 studies, each with only the information provided that it did or did not reach a given alpha level, a counting method (χ^2) gives a very quick test if not a very elegant or powerful estimate of overall probability. With so many studies to process we would probably decide against the blocking method on the grounds that the work required would not be justified by any special benefits. We would not be able to apply the basic method of adding probabilities for reasons given earlier. Most other methods are applicable, however.

If we were combining only a very few studies we might favor the method of adding probabilities but avoid both the method of testing the mean Z and the counting methods which do better on larger numbers of studies.

There is no "best" method under all conditions (Birnbaum, 1954) but the one that seems most serviceable under the largest range of conditions is the method of adding Zs, with or without weighting. When the number of studies is small, it can be suggested in good conscience that at least two other procedures also be employed and the overall ps emerging from all three be reported. When the number of studies is large, a useful combination would seem to be the method of adding Zs combined with one or more of the counting methods as a check. Practical experience with the various methods suggests that there is only rarely a serious discrepancy among appropriately chosen methods. It goes without saying, of course, that any overall p computed (or its associated

Table 3. Advantages and Limitations of Nine Methods of Combining Probabilities

Method	*Advantages*	*Limitations*	*Use When*
Adding Logs	Well-established	Cumulates poorly; can support opposite conclusions.	N of studies small (≤ 5)
Adding *ps*	Good power	Inapplicable when N of studies (or *ps*) large unless complex corrections are introduced.	N of studies small ($\Sigma p \leq 1.0$)
Adding *ts*	Unaffected by N of studies given minimum *df* per study	Inapplicable when *ts* based on very few *df*.	Studies not based on too few *df*
Adding *Zs*	Routinely applicable; simple	Assumes unit variance when under some conditions Type I or Type II errors may be increased.	Anytime
Adding Weighted *Zs*	Routinely applicable; permits weighting	Assumes unit variance when under some conditions Type I or Type II errors may be increased.	Whenever weighting desired
Testing Mean *p*	Simple	N of studies should not be less than four.	N of studies ≥ 4
Testing Mean *Z*	No assumption of unit variance	Low power when N of studies small.	N of studies ≥ 5
Counting	Simple and robust	Large N of studies needed; may be low in power.	N of studies large
Blocking	Displays all means for inspection thus facilitating search for moderator variables	Laborious when N large; insufficient data may be available.	N of studies not too large

test statistic with *df*) should be reported and not suppressed for being "too high" or "too low."

To make possible the computations described in this chapter, authors should routinely report the exact *t, F, Z,* or other test statistic along with its *df* or N rather than simply making such vague statements as "t was significant at $p < .05$." Reporting the test statistic along with an approximate *p* level seems preferable to reporting the "exact" *p* level for several reasons: (1) the exact *p* level may be difficult to determine without a computer, (2) ambiguity about one-tail versus two-tail usage is avoided, and (3) the test statistic allows us to compute exact p as well as the effect size. Speaking of effect size, it would be highly desirable if editors routinely required the report of an effect size (such as d or r) for every test statistic reported.

Finally, it should be noted that even if we have established a low combined p we have said absolutely nothing about the typical size of the effect the "existence" of which we have been examining. We owe it to our readers to give for each combined p estimate an estimate of the probable size of the effect in terms of a σ unit, or a correlation coefficient, or some other estimate (Cohen, 1969). This estimated effect size should be accompanied, when possible, by a confidence interval.

References

Adcock, C. J. "A Note on Combining Probabilities." *Psychometrika,* 1960, *25,* 303–305.

Anderson, R. L., and Bancroft, T. A. *Statistical Theory in Research.* New York: McGraw-Hill, 1952.

Bakan, D. *On Method: Toward a Reconstruction of Psychological Investigation.* San Francisco: Jossey-Bass, 1967.

Baker, P. C. "Combining Tests of Significance in Cross-Validation." *Educational and Psychological Measurement,* 1952, *12,* 300–306.

Bhattacharya, N. "Sampling Experiments on the Combination of Independent χ^2-Tests." *Sankhya: The Indian Journal of Statistics* (Series A), 1961, *23,* 191–196.

Birnbaum, A. "Combining Independent Tests of Significance." *Journal of the American Statistical Association,* 1954, *49,* 559–574.

Brozek, J., and Tiede, K. "Reliable and Questionable Significance in a Series of Statistical Tests." *Psychological Bulletin,* 1952, *49,* 339–341.

Cochran, W. G. "Some Methods for Strengthening the Common χ^2 Tests." *Biometrics,* 1954, *10,* 417–451.

Cochran, W. G., and Cox, G. M. *Experimental Designs.* (2nd ed.) New York: Wiley, 1957.

Cohen, J. *Statistical Power Analysis for the Behavioral Sciences.* (Rev. ed., 1977.) New York: Academic Press, 1969.

DePaulo, B. M., Zuckerman, M., and Rosenthal, R. "Humans as Lie-Detectors." *Journal of Communication,* 1980, *30,* 129–139.

Edgington, E. S. "An Additive Method for Combining Probability Values from Independent Experiments." *Journal of Psychology,* 1972a, *80,* 351–363.

Edgington, E. S. "A Normal Curve Method for Combining Probability Values from Independent Experiments." *Journal of Psychology,* 1972b, *82,* 85–89.

van Elteren, P. "On the Combination of Independent Two Sample Tests of Wilcoxon." *Bulletin de L'Institut International de Statistique,* 1960, *37,* 351–361.

Federighi, E. T. "Extended Tables of the Percentage Points of Student's *t*-Distribution." *Journal of the American Statistical Association,* 1959, *54,* 683–688.

Feldman, K. A. "Using the Work of Others: Some Observations on Reviewing and Integrating." *Sociology of Education,* 1971, *44,* 86–102.

Fisher, R. A. *Statistical Methods for Research Workers.* (7th ed.) London: Oliver and Boyd, 1938.

Fisher, R. A. "Combining Independent Tests of Significance." *American Statistician,* 1948, *2,* 30.

Glass, G. V. "Primary, Secondary, and Meta-Analysis of Research." Paper presented at the meeting of the American Educational Research Association, San Francisco, April 1976.

Good, I. J. "On the Weighted Combination of Significance Tests." *Journal of the Royal Statistical Society: Series B (Methodological),* 1955, *17,* 264–265.

Good, I. J. "Significance Tests in Parallel and in Series." *Journal of the American Statistical Association,* 1958, *53,* 799–813.

Gordon, M. H., Loveland, E. H., and Cureton, E. E. "An Extended Table of Chi-Square for Two Degrees of Freedom, for Use in Combining Probabilities from Independent Samples." *Psychometriks,* 1952, *17,* 311–316.

Greenwald, A. G. "Consequences of Prejudice Against the Null Hypothesis." *Psychological Bulletin,* 1975, *82,* 1–20.

Jones, L. V., and Fiske, D. W. "Models for Testing the Significance of Combined Results." *Psychological Bulletin,* 1953, *50,* 375–382.

Lancaster, H. O. "The Combination of Probabilities Arising from Data in Discrete Distributions." *Biometrika,* 1949, *36,* 370–382.

Lancaster, H. O. "The Combination of Probabilities." *Biometrics,* 1967, *23,* 840–842.

Lancaster, H. O. "The Combination of Probabilities: An Application of Orthonormal Functions." *Australian Journal of Statistics,* 1961, *3,* 20–33.

Light, R. J., and Smith, P. V. "Accumulating Evidence: Procedures for Resolving Contradictions Among Different Research Studies." *Harvard Educational Review,* 1971, *41,* 429–471.

Littell, R. C., and Folks, J. L. "Asymptotic Optimality of Fisher's Method of Combining Independent Tests." *Journal of the American Statistical Association,* 1971, *66,* 802–806.

Luborsky, L., Chandler, M., Auerbach, A. H., Cohen, J., and Bachrach, M. H. "Factors Influencing the Outcome of Psychotherapy: A Review of Quantitative Research." *Psychological Bulletin,* 1971, *75,* 145–185.

McNemar, Q. "At Random: Sense and Nonsense." *American Psychologist,* 1960, *15,* 295–300.

Mosteller, F. M., and Bush, R. R. "Selected Quantitative Techniques." In G. Lindzey (Ed.), *Handbook of Social Psychology.* Vol. 1: *Theory and Method.* Cambridge, Mass.: Addison-Wesley, 1954.

Naylor, A. F. "Small Sample Considerations in Combining 2 × 2 Tables." *Biometrics,* 1967, *23,* 349–356.

Nelson, L. S. "Combining Values of Observed Chi-Squares." *Technometrics,* 1966, *8,* 709.

Oosterhoff, J. "Combination of One-Sided Statistical Tests." In *Mathematical Centre Tracts 28.* Amsterdam: Mathematisch Centrum, 1969.

Pearson, E. S. "The Probability Integral Transformation for Testing Goodness of Fit and Combining Independent Tests of Significance." *Biometrika,* 1938, *30,* 134–148.

Pearson, E. S. "On Questions Raised by the Combination of Tests Based on Discontinuous Distributions." *Biometrika,* 1950, *37,* 383–398.

Pearson, K. "Appendix to Dr. Elderton's Paper on 'The Lanarkshire Milk Experiment.'" *Annals of Eugenics,* 1933, *5,* 337–338.

Puri, M. L. "On the Combination of Independent Two Sample Tests of a General Class." *Review of the International Statistical Institute,* 1965, *33,* 229–241.

Quenouille, M. H. *The Design and Analysis of Experiment.* New York: Wiley, 1952.

Radhakrishna, S. "Combination of Results from Several 2 × 2 Contingency Tables." *Biometrics,* 1965, *21,* 86–98.

Rao, C. R. *Advanced Statistical Methods in Biometric Research.* New York: Hafner, 1953.

Rosenthal, R. "Interpersonal Expectations." In R. Rosenthal and R. L. Rosnow (Eds.), *Artifact in Behavioral Research.* New York: Academic Press, 1969.

Rosenthal, R. *Experimenter Effects in Behavioral Research.* (Enlarged ed.) New York: Irvington, 1976.

Rosenthal, R. "Combining Results of Independent Studies." *Psychological Bulletin,* 1978, *85,* 185–193.

Rosenthal, R. "The 'File Drawer Problem' and Tolerance for Null Results." *Psychological Bulletin,* 1979, *86,* 638–641.

Rosenthal, R., and Gaito, J. "The Interpretation of Levels of Significance by Psychological Researchers." *Journal of Psychology,* 1963, *55,* 33–38.
Rosenthal, R., and Gaito, J. "Further Evidence for the Cliff Effect in the Interpretation of Levels of Significance." *Psychological Reports,* 1964, *15,* 570.
Rosenthal, R., and Rosnow, R. L. *The Volunteer Subject.* New York: Wiley-Interscience, 1975.
Rosenthal, R., and Rubin, D. B. "Interpersonal Expectancy Effects: The First 345 Studies." *The Behavioral and Brain Sciences,* 1978, *3,* 377–415.
Rosenthal, R., and Rubin, D. B. "Comparing Significance Levels of Independent Studies." *Psychological Bulletin,* 1979, *86,* 1165–1168.
Rosenthal, R., and Rubin, D. B. "A Simple, General Purpose Index of Magnitude of Experimental Effect." Unpublished manuscript, Harvard University, 1980.
Smart, R. G. "The Importance of Negative Results in Psychological Research." *Canadian Psychologist,* 1964, *5a,* 225–232.
Snedecor, G. W., and Cochran, W. G. *Statistical Methods.* (6th ed.) Ames: Iowa State University Press, 1967.
Sterling, T. D. "Publication Decisions and Their Possible Effects on Inferences Drawn from Tests of Significance—or Vice Versa." *Journal of the American Statistical Association,* 1959, *54,* 30–34.
Stouffer, S. A., Suchman, E. A., DeVinney, L. C., Star, S. A., and Williams, R. M., Jr. *The American Soldier: Adjustment During Army Life.* Vol. 1. Princeton, N.J.: Princeton University Press, 1949.
Taveggia, T. C. "Resolving Research Controversy Through Empirical Cumulation: Toward Reliable Sociological Knowledge." *Sociological Methods and Research,* 1974, *2,* 395–407.
Wallis, W. A. "Compounding Probabilities from Independent Significance Tests." *Econometrica,* 1942, *10,* 229–248.
Wilkinson, B. "A Statistical Consideration in Psychological Research." *Psychological Bulletin,* 1951, *48,* 156–158.
Winer, B. J. *Statistical Principles in Experimental Design.* (2nd ed.) New York: McGraw-Hill, 1971.
Yates, F. "A Note on the Application of the Combination of Probabilities Test to a Set of 2 × 2 Tables." *Biometrika,* 1955, *42,* 404–411.
Zelen, M., and Joel, L. S. "The Weighted Compounding of Two Independent Significance Tests." *Annals of Mathematical Statistics,* 1959, *30,* 885–895.

Robert Rosenthal is professor of social psychology at Harvard University. His major research interests include interpersonal expectancy effects, nonverbal communication, and social research methods. He is the author of Experimenter Effects in Behavioral Research *and co-author with Lenore Jacobson of* Pygmalion in the Classroom.

Both overall and comparative analyses are needed to illuminate the literature on a topic such as psychotherapy outcome.

Integrating Studies of Psychotherapy Outcomes

Mary Lee Smith

On any interesting topic in the social sciences hundreds of empirical studies will spring out of laboratories and schools and clinics across the country, performed by doctoral candidates or seasoned researchers, each with slightly different definitions of independent and dependent variables, and inevitably producing conflicting results. By what method can theoreticians or policy-makers find the meaning of this research? Do they believe only the subset of studies written by their colleagues or students? Should they believe only the studies with high internal validity? Must they wait for the one "critical experiment," that mythical study of perfect validity which resolves all the issues?

The authoritative review of research has commonly been the arbiter in reconciling conflicting results from large numbers of studies. But traditional methods of research integration were fashioned to accommodate much smaller bodies of literature than are encountered today. They lacked safeguards against prejudiced application and subjective bias. Indeed, the standards of objectivity, verifiability, replicability, and clarity against which primary empirical research were judged were ignored or forgotten when scholars turned to the problem of integrating the primary evidence. Narrative integrations are attempts to portray multiple findings in a connected, verbal report; they are written like stories, sometimes with themes, dramatis personnae, and even a denouement. They can be entertaining, but they seldom portray a body of literature as it really is.

The narrative method of research integration may have emanated from an epistemology of uniformity, an expectation of consistent findings from homogeneous materials such as a physicist might expect to see. The method was ill equipped to cope with the variability of social sciences. As time passed and literature grew to enormous dimensions, the problems of narrative integration became more acute. The impossibility of reading several hundred experiments, reflecting on their findings, and then writing a narrative description was clearly apparent. After all, who would suggest to an experimenter that he merely gaze at the two hundred scores his laboratory animals produced, reflect on them, then write a story about his experiment?

To retain the narrative approach, reviewers had to find ways of reducing a field of dozens or hundreds of studies to only a few. Various strategies of exclusion have been followed. One of the most common is simply to ignore huge areas of the literature where much work lies readily available; the doctoral dissertation literature is a prominent example.

The principal means that narrative reviewers have used to cut a large literature down to manageable size is to exclude the majority of studies through a series of arbitrary stipulative definitions of concepts and a priori judgments of quality. If experimental designs are not of a certain type, if measurement is "unreliable," if statistical analysis is handled ineptly, the findings of the study are thrown away. These methodological rules, learned as dicta in graduate school and regarded as the touchstone of publishable articles in prestigious journals, were applied arbitrarily. But the true purpose of exclusionary tactics was well served: most of the literature was eliminated, and the few studies that survived were at least consistent, if not actually representative of the population of research studies.

Although our initial interests were in the methods of integrating research, after a closer analysis of the history of psychotherapy research and reviews thereof, our interest became more substantive. The effectiveness of psychotherapy remained unclear despite (or perhaps because of) twenty years of acrimonious debate—a war in which the research review was the primary weaponry. Eysenck's original conclusion was based on an invidious comparison of studies from different populations: "[The data] fail to prove that psychotherapy, Freudian or otherwise, facilitates the recovery of neurotic patients. They show that two-thirds of a group of neurotic patients will recover or improve to a marked extent within about two years of the onset of their illness, whether they are treated by means of psychotherapy or not (Eysenck, 1952, p. 322). Rachman's (1971) later conclusion—that there is no evidence to prove the effectiveness of psychotherapy and that the burden of proof remains with those who advocate it—was based on arbitrary and high-handed dismissal on methodological grounds of studies that supported the efficacy of psychotherapy.

These conclusions were based on the narrative method of reviewing psychotherapy research and conflicted with conclusions of subsequent reviews (Luborsky, Singer, and Luborsky, 1975; Meltzoff and Kornreich, 1970) that used the box-score method for integrating research and found the number of positive studies outweighing the negative ones. In the box-score method (Light and Smith, 1971), the reviewer tallies the number of significant and non-significant studies (for and against the hypothesis) and bases his conclusions on the category of greatest frequency. This method is an improvement over impressionistic narrative reviewing methods, but places too much importance on statistical significance as a criterion for categorizing studies, does not avoid completely the problem of arbitrary exclusion of studies, and tells nothing about the magnitude of the effect of psychotherapy.

Better methods were needed for drawing the dominant message from scores of separate studies. Such methods must meet three basic requirements: (1) studies should not be excluded from consideration on arbitrary and a priori grounds; boundaries must be drawn around fields, but it is better to draw them wide than narrow; (2) study findings should be transformed to commensurable expressions of magnitude of experimental effect or correlational relationship; (3) features of studies that might mediate their findings should be defined, measured, and their covariation with findings should be studied. It is assumed that the only data consistently available to the reviewer are those that appear in written reports of a study, which rarely contain raw data. Hence the methods developed must begin with the results of data analyses (means, variances, t-tests, and the like) that are typically reported by researchers. An integrative analysis is then carried out on the results of the primary data analyses. This analysis of analyses, or *meta-analysis,* then becomes the means by which studies are integrated and understood.

Specific meta-analytic techniques were developed by Glass (1976, 1977, and in this volume) and applied to several bodies of literature in education and the social sciences. The results of the extended psychotherapy meta-analysis appears in Smith, Glass, and Miller (1980). The problem addressed in that meta-analysis was as follows: What does the literature as a whole reveal about the effects of psychotherapy? In this chapter the methods used and some of the results will be described.

Methods

The purpose of the meta-analysis was to determine the state of knowledge about the effects of psychotherapy. The population of interest consisted of all controlled studies on the effectiveness of psychotherapy. "Controlled studies" refers to those research investigations in which the experimenter treated one group of clients with a form of psychotherapy, while another more or less comparable group remained untreated, were put on a waiting list for a period of time equal to the time of treatment, received a "placebo" treatment, or received a second form of psychotherapy.

The definition of "psychotherapy" use was liberal, but defensible. More stringent definitions would have ruled out large bodies of pertinent evidence. Our aim was to eliminate the possibilities of the bias that is always introduced into a review when some forms of treatment are arbitrarily excluded. No form of psychotherapy was excluded from the population definition if the therapy (1) involved clients identified by themselves or others as having some emotional or behavioral problem; (2) if the clients sought treatment or were referred for treatment to ameliorate this problem; (3) if the treatment or intervention was psychological or behavioral; and (4) if the person delivering the treatment was identified as a psychotherapist by virtue of training or professional affiliation. Within this definition are studies of the effects of psychodynamic psychotherapy, behavior therapies, cognitive therapies, client-centered therapy, hypnotherapy (when used for psychological and psychosomatic problems), transactional analysis, and eclectic forms of psychotherapy. Studies of vocational and personal counseling were included when their characteristics conformed to the above definition. Studies which might have been called "analogue" by Luborsky (Luborsky, Singer, and Luborsky, 1975) were included in the meta-analysis provided that the therapies coincided with the four-part definition above.

To locate and assemble studies, standard search procedures were used. The studies named by previous reviewers were obtained. *Psychological Abstracts* was searched as was *Educational Resources Information Clearinghouse* (ERIC), and studies named in relevant abstracts were gathered. Journals known to publish outcome studies were searched from their initial volumes to 1977. The bibliographies of studies obtained by the above methods were searched for related research. Colleagues familiar with early phases of the project provided further leads or sent unpublished works. Papers delivered at meetings of such associations as the American Psychological Association and Society for Psychotherapy Research were obtained. *Dissertation Abstracts* in psychology and education were searched from 1900 to 1977. Microfilms of theses that fit the population definition were purchased.

We failed to exhaust the defined population for various reasons. Some studies simply slipped through the net of our search. Studies published in some foreign journals were probably missed. Approximately fifty studies were unused because the statistics reported in them escaped even our tenacious attempts to convert them into common metrics. Sampling procedures were used in two areas where studies were numerous. Dissertation studies of ordinary school counseling were sampled at a rate of 25 percent. About 10 percent of the studies of systematic desensitization of snake anxiety were omitted.

Finally, approximately thirty studies were omitted because they were not fully analyzed before we reached the deadline for proceeding with subsequent steps in the meta-analysis. Decisions to omit studies were not related to any characteristic of the study or to its results. Four hundred seventy-five studies were fully analyzed and account for the conclusions reached in the analyses.

Once obtained, the studies were read and their various features described quantitatively. One objective of the meta-analysis was to investigate the relationship between the effect produced by the therapy in a study and other features of the study such as the characteristics of the clients, the type of therapy, the type of outcome, and the like. To do this, it was necessary to develop a coding form on which the important characteristics could be described and quantified. It covers items of information described below:

Date of Publication
Source of Publication (journal, book, dissertation, or unpublished paper)
Professional Affiliation of Experimenter (psychology, education, social work, or "other")
Experimenter Blinding (degree of blinding in assignment of clients to treatment groups and in assessment of outcomes; rated either "single blind," "experimenter did therapy," or "experimenter knew composition of groups but did not personally treat the client")
Client Diagnosis (neurotic, complex phobic, monosymptom phobic, psychotic, "normal," character disordered, delinquent or felon, addicted, emotional-somatic disordered, handicapped, depressive, or "other"; conventions were developed to sort clients into diagnostic types)
Hospitalization (number of years client had been hospitalized prior to study)
Client Intelligence (a group average estimated roughly as high, average, or low)
Client-Therapist Similarity (ethnic, socio-economic status, and health of client and similarity with therapist)
Solicitation of Clients (subjects independently sought help, were referred, committed involuntarily, or were solicited for therapy by the experimenter)
Assignment of Clients to Groups (random assignment to treatment or control group, matched groups, non-equivalent control groups; this feature is the best determinant of the rigor of the study)
Experimental Mortality (the percentages of treatment group and control groups which terminate before the end of the study)
Internal Validity (assessment of the rigor of the experimental design, based on assignment of subject to groups and degree of mortality from samples)
Allegiance of the Experimenter (a judgment of the degree of enthusiasm or faith of the experimenter in one form of treatment over another)
Therapy Modality (individual, group, mixed, other)
Therapy Location (school, hospital, mental health center, college facility, prison, residential facility, or other)
Therapy Duration (the number of hours of therapy and the number of weeks covered by the treatment)
Therapist Experience (the number of years of experience of the therapist)
Type of Outcome (fear or anxiety, self-esteem, ratings of global adjustment, life indicators of adjustment, personality traits, measures of emotional-somatic disorders, measures of addiction, sociopathic behaviors, social behaviors, work or school achievement, measures

of vocational or personal development, or physiological measures of stress; conventions were developed to sort outcome measures into these outcome types)

Reactivity of Outcome Measure (Highly *reactive* instruments are those which reveal or closely parallel the obvious goals or valued outcomes of the therapist who has an acknowledged interest in achieving pre-determined goals, or which are subject to the client's need and ability to alter his scores to show more or less change than what actually took place. Relatively non-reactive measures are not so easily influenced in any direction by any of the parties involved)

Follow-Up Time (the number of weeks between the end of therapy and the collection of outcome data)

Type of Therapy (treatments were categorized, according to conventions, as follows: psychodynamic, dynamic eclectic, Adlerian, hypnotherapy, client-centered, gestalt, rational-emotive or other cognitive, reality therapy, transactional analysis, behavior modification, implosion, systematic desensitization, cognitive behavioral, eclectic behavioral, or placebo; therapy types were grouped into Behavioral and Verbal classes by scaling procedures)

Once features of the studies were quantified, the magnitude of therapeutic effect was computed. Nearly all previous reviewers of psychotherapy outcome research have relied on the statistical significance of the differences between therapy and control groups to indicate whether that study supported or failed to support therapy effectiveness. However, using statistical significance confounds the magnitude of the effect produced by a treatment with the size of the sample and other technical features of the experiment independent of the treatment effect. Therefore, a statistic was chosen to represent only the magnitude of therapeutic effect. The definition of the magnitude of effect—or "effect size"—was the mean difference between the treated and control subjects divided by the standard deviation of the control group, that is, $\Delta_{T-C} = (\overline{X}_T - \overline{X}_C)/s_C$. An effect size of +1 indicates that a person at the mean of the control group would be expected to rise to the 84th percentile of the control group if he were given treatment.

Calculating effect sizes was straightforward for those studies with means and standard deviations reported. If means and standard deviations were not reported, effect sizes were obtained by solving equations from t- or F-ratios or from other inferential statistics. Statistical procedures for solving these equations followed Glass (1977). Probit transformations were used to convert percentages (such as improvement rates) to effect sizes (Glass, 1977). Original data were requested from several authors when effect sizes could not be derived from any reported information. Effect sizes were calculated on each non-redundant outcome measure the researcher reported. A measure was judged to be redundant only if it was like another in (1) outcome type, (2) reactivity of measure, (3) follow-up time, *and* (4) magnitude of effect. Almost every study yielded more than one non-redundant measure, each of which was converted into an effect size. Four hundred and seventy-five studies produced about 1,760 effect sizes. This method introduced non-independence into the data set. To have achieved independence by using the study as the unit of analysis would have required computing an average effect size for all outcome variables within a study. Thus if a particular study employed outcomes as discrepant as the Galvanic Skin Response and the Fear Thermometer, the results from these two would have been averaged into a single effect size. An empirical estimate of the relationship between magnitude of effect and type of measurement would have been impossible. If a particular study assessed effects immediately after therapy and then two years later, the two findings would have to be averaged to achieve statistical independence. The relationship between magnitude of effect and the follow-up time of measurement would have been lost. Therefore, in our judgment, the danger of non-independence was offset by the significant increase in the quantity and quality of information afforded by the decision to use each outcome variable rather than each study as the unit of analysis.

Examples of Coded Studies

To illustrate the process of classifying the features of the study two examples are presented. Willis and Edwards (1969) published a study of the effects of systematic desensitization and implosion on mouse phobia. Krumboltz and Thoresen (1964) published a study of the effect of behavioral counseling on vocational information-seeking behavior. Table 1 contains the results of coding these studies and the reasons for the coding when judgments were made.

Data Analysis

Meta-analysis is the analysis of analyses. The effect sizes, calculated from the statistical results of separate studies, are treated as the dependent variable in the meta-analysis. Independent variables are the characteristics of the study, the clients, the treatment, and the outcomes.

Using the data from all studies, several analyses were performed. First, descriptive statistics on the characteristics of the data were obtained. Second, all continuous variables, including effect size, were intercorrelated. Third, discrete variables were crosstabulated (such as therapies with outcomes, diagnoses with outcomes). Fourth, average effect sizes ($\bar{\Delta}$) were obtained for different values of all the independent variables. For example, average effect sizes were obtained for each diagnostic type, each outcome type, each level of internal validity and reactivity. In this way, it is possible to determine, using the studies as a whole, the comparative effects of clients, treatments, and outcomes. Cautions in interpreting these comparisons must be noted, however. For example, a comparison of the magnitude of effect associated with long-

Table 1. Classification of Studies by Willis and Edwards (1969) and Krumboltz and Thoreson (1964)

	Willis and Edwards	*Krumboltz and Thoreson*
Publication Date	1969	1964
Publication Form	Journal	Journal
Training of Experimenter	Psychology (judged from institutional affiliation)	Education (known by institutional affiliation)
Blinding	Experimenter did therapy (judged from tone of the report)	Experimenter (evaluators) did not do therapy but did know group composition (no information about blinding of evaluators was given)
Diagnosis	Mouse phobic, simple phobic (no indication given of neurotic symptoms other than anxiety to rodent)	Vocationally undecided (students who asked for counseling about future plans, grouped in "neurotic" diagnostic type)
Hospitalization	None	None
Intelligence	Above average (inferred from client status as college student)	Average (estimated, in the absence of other information)
Client–Therapist Similarity	Very similar (inferred from client degree of disturbance and status as college student)	Moderately similar (ages differed, but socioeconomic status of community indicated similarity)
Age	20 (inferred from college student status)	16 (high school juniors)
Percent Male	0% (stated as all-female population)	50% (sample stratified by client sex)
Solicitation of Client	Solicited by experimenter (stated as solicited based on extreme pre-test scores)	Clients volunteered after being given notice that counseling would be available
Assignment of Clients to Groups	Random (stated as matched groups on pre-test measure, then random assignment to 3 groups)	Random (stated)
Assignment of Therapist	Non-random (no therapist differences produced in outcomes)	Random

Experimental Mortality	0% in all groups at termination; 4% in all groups at follow-up (stated)	No subjects lost from any group (stated)
Internal Validity	High (based on random assignment and low mortality, although the design suffered from threats to internal validity of testing and instrumentation)	High
Simultaneous Comparison	Yes (systematic desensitization against implosion against control)	Yes (2 treatment groups and placebo group compared against control)
Type of Treatment	(1) Systematic Desensitization—Behavioral subclass (2) Implosion—Behavioral subclass	(1) Model Reinforcement—Cognitive Behavioral subclass (students were shown tapes of models being reinforced for information-seeking behavior but students were not reinforced personally) (2) Verbal Reinforcement—Behavioral subclass (counselors verbally reinforced clients for production of information-seeking statements) (3) Film Discussion–Placebo (clients saw and discussed a film, to control for non-specific effects of counselor attention)
Confidence of Classification	Rated 4 (based on inclusion of key concept and references and the commonality from experiment to experiment using these therapies)	Rated 5 (highest) (because of thoroughness of description, knowledge of experimenter's theory and previous work)
Allegiance	Write-up showed no general favorability toward either treatment over the other	Equal allegiance paid to each of treatments. No allegiance to placebo condition
Modality	Individual treatment (stated)	Mixed (students were randomly assigned to individual and group treatments, but modality did not interact with outcome, so the two modes were combined for the meta-analysis)
Location	College facility (stated)	School (stated)
Duration	3 hours over 3 weeks (stated that the average client required 5 sessions of 25 minutes for relaxation training and hierarchy presentation; exact duration had to be estimated from these figures)	2 hours, 2 weeks (2 sessions, time estimated)

Table 1. Classification of Studies by Willis and Edwards (1969) and Krumboltz and Thoreson (1964) (continued)

	Willis and Edwards	*Krumboltz and Thoreson*
Therapist Experience	5 years (no information given, coding conventions allow 5 years for Ph.D. level psychologists)	2 years (estimated by status in counselor-training program plus training for this experiment)
Outcome	3 outcome measures were used: the Fear Survey Schedule (FSS, total) the Fear Thermometer, and the Behavior Avoidance Measure (BAT). The result from the Fear Thermometer paralleled those of the other two and thus was omitted. Follow-up data were reported in such a way that effect sizes were impossible to calculate. Both the BAT and the FSS were classified as measures of fear-anxiety. They were given immediately after therapy. They were rated as 5 on the reactivity scale because the scales were used as part of the treatment, the behavioral measure was taken by the non-blinded experimenter.	Two outcome measures were used: Frequency and Variety of information-seeking behavior as estimated from responses to structured interview questions. Reactivity was rated "4" for both because measures were self-report of clients to non-blinded evaluators. These were classified as measures of vocational or personal development.
Effect Size	Statistics were reported in the form of mean differences between groups and F-statistics from a 3-factor ANOVA. The effect sizes were as follows:	Statistics reported as treatment means and mean squares from a 4-factor analysis of variance. The effect sizes were as follows:

Willis and Edwards effect sizes:

	FSS	*BAT*
Systematic Desensitization	1.71	.07
Implosion	2.12	.48

Krumboltz and Thoreson effect sizes:

	Frequency of Information-Seeking Behavior	*Variety of Information-Seeking Behavior*
Model Reinforcement	1.29	.77
Verbal Reinforcement	1.05	1.39
Placebo	.21	.27

term (twenty or more sessions) versus short-term (ten or fewer sessions) therapy is not an experimental comparison. Therapies of longer duration are likely to be used with more seriously disturbed clients. Certain types of therapy tend to be shorter and have more modest goals. These and other factors must be rival hypotheses in the interpretation of the difference in effect that is due to length of therapy.

Statistical controls were instituted to estimate more accurately the comparative effectiveness of different therapies. Cross-classification of independent variables was used to determine, for example, the average effect of each therapy type on clients in various diagnostic categories (for example, the effect of psychodynamic therapy on neurotics versus psychotics, the effect of client-centered therapy on measures of self-esteem versus measures of fear and anxiety). Multiple regression analysis was performed: the dependent variable was the effect size and the independent variables were determined by studying the intercorrelations generated earlier. Using multiple regression allowed the examination of the relationship of each independent variable with effect size with all other independent variables held constant.

The most important analysis was the "same-experiment" analysis, which involved only that subset of studies in which an experimenter compared *within a single study* the effects of a Behavioral therapy and a Verbal therapy. For example, an experimenter might have compared three groups: one which received eclectic psychotherapy (Verbal therapy class), one which received systematic desensitization (Behavior therapy class), and one which received no treatment (control group). Within the "same experiment" data set, all variables unrelated to the therapy would be the same for both therapy groups—the same outcome measure would be used for both groups, they would be treated for the same length of time with therapists of approximately the same degree of ability, and the diagnostic type would be the same for both therapies. All other pre-existing client variables would be comparable in the three groups by virtue of random assignment or matching. Thus the comparative effectiveness of therapies could be more accurately estimated from the "same experiment" data than in the data as a whole. However, one important variable could not be controlled and that was the allegiance of the experimenter. Often one therapy in a study was obviously the favorite; the other, the also-ran.

Results

The results of the meta-analysis showed unequivocally that psychotherapy is effective. Estimated for all types of therapy, client, and outcome, the average effect was .85 standard deviation units. This estimate is based on 475 controlled studies, 1,766 measured effects, and tens of thousands of persons. In relative terms, the effect of .85 standard deviations means this: a person who is no better off than average (is at the 50th percentile) in psychological well being compared to all those who have not received psychotherapy rises to the 80th percentile as a result of psychotherapy. At the end of treatment, he is better off than 80 percent of those who need therapy but remain untreated.

The question of comparative effectiveness of different types of therapy did not yield a single answer. At the simplest level, therapies were merely compared for average effectiveness, disregarding any systematic differences in the kinds of client typically treated by each therapy and the types of outcomes typically observed. This simple, uncontrolled comparison yields results such as the following. Cognitive, cognitive-behavioral therapies, hypnotherapy, and systematic desensitization appeared most effective. "Undifferentiated counseling" was least effective. Psychodynamic, dynamic-eclectic, Adlerian, client-centered, gestalt, rational-emotive therapies, transactional analysis, implosive therapy, behavior modification, eclectic-behavioral therapy, and vocational-personal development counseling were close to the average effectiveness of all therapies. Placebo treatments, usually consisting of relaxation training or mere attention from a therapist, showed a positive effect as large as one-half standard deviation unit, but about half as large as the therapy effect estimated from those studies that used placebos. Organized into classes of therapy, and using no controls, the Behavioral therapies ($\bar{\Delta} = .98$) were more effective than the Verbal therapies ($\bar{\Delta} = .85$).

A more complex and sophisticated treatment of the comparative effectiveness question included making allowances for the systematically different characteristics of clients and outcomes typical of the various types of therapy. Once these varying characteristics were controlled or canceled out as was done with regression analysis and the "same experiment" data, a different picture emerged. The well-controlled comparisons yielded no reliable differences in effectiveness of Behavioral and Verbal therapies (see Table 2).

The characteristics of the clients involved in the therapy evaluation influenced the size of effects eventually produced. Depressed clients and clients with simple, monosymptomatic phobias were associated with the largest effects ($\bar{\Delta} \sim 1.10$); psychotics, neurotics, and handicapped clients with the smallest ($\bar{\Delta} \sim .61$). The more intelligent the client, the more alike the therapist and client in education and socioeconomic status, the larger the therapeutic effect was likely to be. The greater the proportion of female clients, the larger was the effect.

Many theoreticians demand of research the answer to the problem of "What therapy for what client in what setting?" Yet even with a data base as large as this one, answering that question was impossible. Cross-tabulating therapy type with diagnostic type with outcome type yielded almost no stable estimates of effects.

The characteristics of a therapy, other than its theoretical classification, bore surprisingly little relation to the size of effect. Individual therapy and group therapy and combinations of them were equally effective. The duration of therapy was unrelated to its measured effectiveness (r between Δ and "hours of therapy" = $-.05$). The experience of the therapist was unrelated to therapeutic effectiveness, although the years of experience of therapists in the studies was quite low, on the average (r between Δ and therapist experience = .01; average experience = 3.19 years).

Table 2. The Comparative Effectiveness of Verbal and Behavioral Therapies

Type of Comparison	*Average Effect Size (△)*	*Standard Error (△)*	*Number of Effects*
Uncontrolled			
Verbal Therapies	.85	.05	597
Behavioral Therapies	.98	.04	791
Regression Adjusted			
Verbal Therapies	.88	.06	597
Behavioral Therapies	.91	.07	791
"Same Experiment" Analysis			
Verbal Therapies:			
Psychological Measures*	.83	.05	133
Life Measures	.53	.08	42
Behavioral Therapies:			
Psychological Measures	1.07	.05	130
Life Measures	.52	.11	40

*Psychological measures were fear-anxiety, self-esteem, global adjustment, personality traits, vocational-personal development. Life measures, less susceptible to influence, were life adjustment, emotional-somatic complaint, addiction, sociopathic behaviors, work or school achievement, and physiological stress.

Interesting variations in magnitude of therapeutic effect were produced by the methods of the studies. The allegation by critics of psychotherapy—that poor quality research methods account for the positive outcomes observed—can now be laid to rest. The degree of experimental rigor employed by the researcher was *positively,* although weakly, related to the size of effect produced ($r = .03$). Greater controls were associated with slightly higher effects. Experimental mortality and the degree of blinding in the evaluation were also unrelated to outcome.

Yet other features of the experiment were in fact influential in determining effect size. Clients who were solicited by the experimenter especially for the study or who heard of therapy through advertisements of special therapy programs were associated with the largest effects. Smaller effects were associated with clients who recognized their problems and sought assistance on their own and those who were committed to therapy as part of a hospital or prison program. These last categories are probably the most representative of actual therapeutic practice. Experimenter allegiance should also be viewed critically. Almost 60 percent of the treatments were tested by researchers with recognizable allegiance to the therapy. This positive allegiance was associated with larger effects.

The choice of outcome criteria was most important in determining the magnitude of effects observed in a study. All types of outcome measurement showed positive effects, but some types were associated with greater effects than others. Measures of fear or anxiety were associated with the largest effects ($\bar{\Delta} = 1.12$). Measures of work or school achievement showed the smallest effects ($\bar{\Delta} = .49$). The reactivity of the method used to measure the outcome was also associated with the magnitude of effect measured in a study. Those measures that were "reactive"—easy to influence and obvious as to the social desirability of response—were associated with the greater magnitudes of effect. The time the evaluator chose to measure the outcome also affected the estimate of therapeutic effect. If measured immediately after therapy, the magnitude of effect was about .90 standard deviation units. This effect drops gradually to about .50 if the effect is measured two years after therapy. The measurement of outcomes was critical to answering the question of comparative therapeutic effectiveness. Compared to Verbal therapies, Behavioral therapies were evaluated using more highly reactive measures and assessments were made closer to the end of therapy. These differences may account for what appeared to be the superiority of Behavioral over Verbal therapy when the two were compared without controls.

As a case of research integration the psychotherapy meta-analysis presented a variety of interesting methodological problems which have since been addressed in more detail in Glass, Smith, and Barton (1979). To settle the substantive debate is too optimistic. A more realistic standard for judging the merits of this work is whether, by providing a quantitative estimate of the effects of psychotherapy based on the research literature as a whole, discussion about the effects of psychotherapy has been improved.

References

Eysenck, H. J. "The Effects of Psychotherapy: An Evaluation." *Journal of Consulting Psychology,* 1952, *16,* 319–324.

Glass, G. V. "Primary, Secondary, and Meta-Analysis of Research." *Educational Researcher,* 1976, *5,* 3–8.

Glass, G. V. "Integrating Findings: The Meta-Analysis of Research." In L. Shulman (Ed.), *Review of Research in Education,* 1977, *5,* 351–379.

Glass, G. V, Smith, M. L., and Barton, M. "Methods of Integrative Analysis." Annual Report on Grant NIE-G-78-0148. Boulder, Colo.: Laboratory of Educational Research, University of Colorado, 1979.

Krumboltz, J. D., and Thoreson, C. E. "The Effects of Behavioral Counseling in Group and Individual Settings on Information-Seeking Behavior." *Journal of Counseling Psychology,* 1964, *11,* 324–333.

Light, R. J., and Smith, P. V. "Accumulating Evidence: Procedures for Resolving Contradictions Among Different Research Studies." *Harvard Educational Review,* 1971, *41,* 429–471.

Luborsky, L., Singer, B., and Luborsky, L. "Comparative Studies of Psychotherapies." *Archives of General Psychiatry,* 1975, *32,* 995–1008.

Meltzoff, J., and Kornreich, M. *Research in Psychotherapy.* Chicago: Aldine, 1970.

Rachman, S. *The Effects of Psychotherapy.* Oxford: Pergamon Press, 1971.

Smith, M. L., Glass, G. V, and Miller, T. I. *The Benefits of Psychotherapy.* Baltimore: The John Hopkins University Press, 1980.

Willis, R. W., and Edwards, J. A. "A Study of the Comparative Effectiveness of Systematic Desensitization and Implosive Therapy." *Behavioral Research and Therapy,* 1969, *7,* 387–395.

Mary Lee Smith is assistant professor in the Laboratory of Educational Research, University of Colorado. In addition to research on psychotherapy and on school class-size, she has pursued her interest in methods of naturalistic inquiry, conducting ethnographic studies on science and mathematics teaching, special education, and alternative education.

Although procedures and results have varied over decades, the techniques of meta-analysis make it easy to demonstrate that women and girls excel in the skills of identifying and sending nonverbal messages of emotion.

Gender Differences in Nonverbal Communication Skills

Judith A. Hall

In this chapter I shall apply some of the concepts of meta-analysis to the study of gender differences. Gender is an ideal independent variable for such an analysis because of the high reliability and accuracy of its measurement. With gender, unlike many experimentally manipulated variables, there is little fear of slippage between the conceptual variable and its operationalization. Of course, how one interprets gender differences—for example, whether gender is seen as a biological or a social variable—is not so unambiguous, but that is a theoretical issue which fortunately does not need to be resolved here.

Background

If there is a key feature of women's mystique, it is probably some kind of special social sensitivity or social ability that they are believed to possess. An apt example occurs in one of the final, and climactic, scenes of George Eliot's *Adam Bede.* Throughout the novel, Adam has loved Sue from afar. Now, Adam's mother announces that Sue also loves Adam. Asked if Sue has said anything of the sort, the mother replies that Sue would never say anything about it. Pressed further, the mother explains that she knew it from Sue's tendency to tremble in Adam's presence. Her observation, "It's on'y the men as have to wait till folks say things afore they find 'em out," captures the common belief about women. Perhaps only a woman author would have phrased it so flatteringly to women; more commonly, women's "intuition" is seen, and has been seen for centuries, as a second-rate skill compared to logical, rational, and analytical inference (West, 1979).

Intuition has a long philosophical and literary history that is beyond the scope of this chapter. Because of its rich connotations, it is an imprecise concept that can mean a variety of things including the ability to "know" something without any apparent cognitive processing or even to "know" something without any observable data to go on, as in mind-reading and clairvoyance. The sense most relevant here involves some kind of insight into people—their motives, needs, and moods—as well as a grasp of how to act toward others. In terms of objectively measured ability, the closest counterparts to this definition seem to be the abilities to read and send nonverbal cues. There are, of course, other social skills that might also be called intuition, but these have been rarely or never measured. An example would be the kind of knowledge of "human nature" and of social situations that would enable one to pick the most appropriate actions toward others in a variety of situations and for a variety of purposes. This is not the same as nonverbal sending skill because knowing what is socially appropriate and being able to do it are conceptually distinct skills.

Researchers have been comparing men and women on ability to decode nonverbal expressions for over fifty years, and have been comparing them on ability to encode nonverbal expressions, though not as often, for forty years. As I will try to demonstrate, it was possible to conclude with some confidence from early on that women excelled in both kinds of skills. But despite an almost constant stream of published findings on gender differences in decoding skill, authors' attempts to summarize the literature have shown a surprising lack of confidence, and when two recent reviewers did state their conclusions with confidence, the conclusions were wrong, though in a qualified way as will be seen later. In my mind, the two most likely reasons for this state of affairs are that reviewers over the years did not examine enough of the available literature and that they did not employ the right tools in their attempts to summarize what was known. I will not rule out the additional possibility that reviewers, consciously or not, have been reluctant to *see* these gender differences. Prejudice against women could make some not want to see female superiority; ironically, writers with a feminist orientation might also wish, for their own ideological reasons, to minimize gender differences. Happily, I have no evidence of any kind for the presence of either kind of bias; the possibility comes to mind only because it is hard to understand why, as late as 1977, reviewers were still failing to perform a proper summary, in the case of decoding at least, despite the clear interest and relevance of the issue.

For illustration, authors have said that the decoding literature was "not clear" (Weisgerber, 1956), or "consistently contradictory" (Davitz, 1964), or "somewhat contradictory" (Tagiuri, 1969), or "mixed" (Gitter, Kozel, and Mostofsky, 1972). Two early writers came closer to a proper summary than did some later writers. Jenness (1932, p. 339) said that it was "barely right" that women slightly excel men in judging facial expressions, and Coleman (1949, p. 1) said there were "no major differences" in the ability to judge emotions, but also said "women tend to be slightly superior to men in identification of facial expressions."

Recently, two major reviews reached the conclusion that there are no gender differences in decoding skill. Maccoby and Jacklin (1974), in a review of research on "empathy," included several studies of nonverbal decoding along with studies that measured a variety of other abilities and traits relating to interpersonal responsiveness. They concluded that females were not generally more sensitive to social cues than males, and more specifically, that "neither sex has greater ability to judge the reactions and intentions of others in any generalized sense" (p. 214). Hoffman (1977) drew attention to the heterogeneity of measures called "empathy" in the Maccoby and Jacklin (1974) review, and organized the literature into two categories: "empathy," that is, responding vicariously to others' feelings, and "recognition of affect," a more cognitive ability to judge and label social stimuli. Still, his category of "recognition of affect" was broader than the category of "nonverbal decoding" used in the present chapter, since it included such measures as verbal report of how a story character feels and the tendency to perceive anger in faces. Though he clearly intended to include nonverbal decoding, as indicated by the two decoding studies included in the review, he did not include most of the available decoding studies. On the basis of his recognition of affect category, he concluded that "when encountering someone in an emotional situation, both sexes are equally adept at assessing how that person feels" (1977, p. 716).

In the case of the encoding, rather than decoding, literature, I know of only one major review attempt (Hall, 1977), and the number of studies is fewer. Nevertheless, the scattered summary statements indicate that the picture has seemed less equivocal. Perhaps the idea that women are more expressive than men creates less ambivalence than does the idea that women read emotional cues better than men do. Because tests of decoding skill bear a resemblance to tests of other cognitive skills, to acknowledge women's skill in decoding may seem like acknowledging that they are smarter in some way than men. Their superior encoding skills may be easier to accept because the "skill" may seem more like social role enactment or the uncontrolled expression of emotionality—neither of which implies "real" superiority.

The Decoding Data Set

The data set consists of studies, published or submitted for publication at the time of the review, that measured ability to make correct judgments of emotions or interpersonal dominance communicated via face, body, and voice tone.

In all of the studies, groups of subjects served as judges of nonverbal expressive stimuli consisting of face, body, or vocal cues (alone or in combination), presented via drawings, photos, films, videotapes, standard-content speech, scrambled speech, or electronically filtered speech. In the method of standard-content speech (Davitz and Davitz, 1959) the speakers recite meaningless or affectively ambiguous material, varying the vocal expression to suit the intended emotion. In scrambled speech (Scherer, 1971) an audiotape of a voice is cut into small pieces and randomly reassembled, creating a garbled version of the original utterance. In electronic filtering (Rogers, Scherer, and Rosenthal, 1971), critical bands of frequencies are removed from the voice signal, making the voice sound muffled and the words unintelligible.

The expressive stimuli in these studies were generated in a variety of ways. By far the most common method was to ask the sender or senders to express various emotions, while these expressions were photographed, audiotaped, and so on. The earlier studies often employed standard sets of facial expression stimuli generated in this way. "Spontaneous" expressions were elicited in some studies by presenting subjects with emotion-provoking stimuli and recording their unrehearsed responses (for example, one study used a snake and a crushed snail, and others used affectively arousing slides or videotapes). Other stimuli were photos cut out of magazines, voices of people who were either rested or tired, voices of people who were either lying or telling the truth, and drawings of facial expressions.

Judgments were typically multiple-choice, with the response alternatives describing the possible names of the emotion (for example, happiness, fear, disgust), the interpersonal situation represented in the stimulus (for example, ordering food in a restaurant, telling truth or lying), or the nature of the stimulus that elicited the nonverbal expression being judged (for instance, car accident, pleasant adult-child interaction). The number of response alternatives ranged from two to over twenty-five. Other judging formats included pointing to a photograph after hearing a story, picking the two faces from an array that expressed the most similar emotion, making open-ended verbal responses, and rating degrees of friendliness.

Seventy-five independent samples from forty-two sources are in the data set. More than thirty operationalizations of decoding are included, all of which fit the criteria described above. Attributes of the studies that were coded were: year, sample size, age group of subjects, age group of senders who were judged, gender of the senders, and channel of communication (face, body, and so on). Altogether, some 10,000 individuals were tested in the seventy-five samples.

Outcome Measures. Whenever possible three outcome indices were generated: (1) direction of the effect (female advantage, male advantage, or "no difference"), (2) statistical significance ($p > .05$ versus $p \leq .05$), and (3) size of effect. The effect size index used was Cohen's d, which is defined as the difference between the means of the two groups to be compared divided by their common standard deviation (Cohen, 1977; Friedman, 1968; Rosenthal, this volume). Since d is a "signal-to-noise" index—that is, it indicates the size of a difference relative to uncontrolled variation—it is likely to be larger in very well controlled studies (for example, groups that are homogeneous on extraneous variables), in studies that employ very powerful data analytic techniques, or in studies that employ more reliable and/or valid measuring instruments. But *d* also becomes larger when the mean difference between the groups to be compared grows larger, and this could be due to real change in the magnitude of a phenomenon over time. In the case of gender differences, effects could grow larger (or smaller) over time because of changes in education or in societal expectations. Ambiguity over whether variation in the size of *d* is due to variation in the "signal," the "noise," or both makes *d* sometimes hard to interpret and makes comparison with other indices especially important. For example, if *d* becomes larger over time but the proportion of studies showing male versus female superiority (no matter what the magnitude of the difference) stays about the same, it would suggest that methodological improvements might have led to the larger effects rather than changes in the actual skill levels of the two groups.

In this review, *d* is signed so that positive values indicate female superiority and negative values indicate male superiority. Additional analyses of the data besides those presented here can be found in Hall (1977, 1978, 1979).

Overall Results for Decoding. In Table 1 are summarized the results, pooling over channels (visual, auditory, mixed), gender of stimuli (male, female, both), age of subjects (preschool through post-college), and age of stimuli (children through post-college). Twelve studies reported "no difference" without giving statistics, and two studies showed $d = .00\sigma$; these 14 studies are excluded from the results for direction of effect (first two rows). The two results of $d = .00\sigma$ are included in the computations of mean and median effect sizes, however. The computations of χ^2 for statistical significance (last three rows) are based on different expected frequencies; the first two tests are based on the total number of $p \leq .05$ results favoring women to be expected by chance (.025 of total *N*), and the third test is based on the expected number of significant results favoring women (.50 of *N* of significant studies).

The results of Table 1 are very clear. Women and girls perform better on tests of decoding ability than men and boys do. The mean effect size is just within the range that Cohen (1977) calls moderate and large enough to be visible to the naked eye. Though the mean effect size is not large, the overall combined probability is less than .00003, one-tail (Stouffer method described in Rosenthal, 1978). (Both here and in the encoding review described later, the combined *p* was computed conservatively. Instead of computing the exact probability of each study, a figure that frequently was not shown, each significant study was assumed to be significant at $p = .05$, two-tail, and was assigned a *z* of ± 1.96. This *z* was signed according to the direction of the effect. Results that were non-significant were assigned a *z* of zero. The *z*s were then summed and divided by the square-root of the total number of studies to yield a combined *z*.)

The mean size of the effect varied with the channel of communication

Table 1. Summary of Gender Differences in Nonverbal Communication Skill

Index	*Decoding Studies ($N = 75$)*	*Encoding Studies ($N = 26$)*
Direction of Effect (all studies but excluding findings of no difference)	51 of 61 studies (84%) show female advantage, $\chi^2(1) = 26.23$, $p < .0001$	15 of 21 studies (71%) show female advantage, $\chi^2(1) = 3.05$, $p < .10$
Direction of Effect (studies for which effect size known and excluding findings of no difference)	36 of 44 studies (82%) show female advantage, $\chi^2(1) = 16.57$, $p < .0001$	15 of 19 studies (79%) show female advantage, $\chi^2(1) = 5.26$, $p < .025$
Mean Effect Size (d)	For 46 studies, $d = .40\sigma$, $t(45) = 4.38$, $p < .0001$	For 20 studies, $d = .66\sigma$, $t(19) = 2.76$, $p < .02$
Mean Effect Size (d) Weighted for Sample N	For 46 studies, $d = .34\sigma$ (not tested)	For 20 studies, $d = .52\sigma$ (not tested)
Median Effect Size (d)	For 46 studies, $d = .32\sigma$ (not tested)	For 20 studies, $d = .62\sigma$ (not tested)
Statistical Significance (all studies)	23 of 75 studies (31%) show significant female advantage, $\chi^2(1) = 65.62$, $p < .0001$*	8 of 26 studies (31%) show significant female advantage, $\chi^2(1) = 50.96$, $p < .0001$
Statistical Significance (studies for which effect size known)	22 of 46 studies (48%) show significant female advantage, $\chi^2(1) = 61.09$, $p < .0001$*	8 of 20 studies (40%) show significant female advantage, $\chi^2(1) = 51.58$, $p < .0001$
Statistical Significance (statistically significant studies)	23 of 24 studies (96%) that are significant show female advantage, $\chi^2(1) = 18.38$, $p < .0001$	8 of 9 studies (89%) that are significant show female advantage, $\chi^2(1) = 5.44$, $p < .02$

*These chi-square tests were computed conservatively: The expected frequency of significant studies was set at a minimum of 5, which was considerably greater than an expected frequency of .025 times N would have been. This procedure was not done in the encoding review below because the small N of cases did not stand up to such a conservative procedure.

employed, from a low of $.18\sigma$ for auditory cues (10 studies), to a high of 1.020 for studies with mixed visual and auditory cues (7 studies). The largest category, visual cues (face and/or body) showed a mean effect of $.32\sigma$ (29 studies). The large mean effect for mixed cues (which was significantly larger than the other two categories combined, $t(43) = 3.23$, ($p = .002$) may be due to the fact that mixed-cue studies tended to be very recent and seem to have employed more precise instruments (based on more items, for instance) and more sophisticated data analysis than did the earlier studies.

Other relationships between characteristics of the studies and their outcomes were efficiently assessed by recoding a number of variables that were non-ordered trichotomies into dichotomies (for example, male versus female senders, excluding studies with both; visual versus auditory cues, excluding studies with mixed cues), and computing product-moment correlations among all the variables. One very instructive result of this analysis was the correlation of .06 ($df = 44$) between effect size and age group of the subjects. This tells that there is no interaction of the subjects' gender and age (that is, the average difference between males and females is more or less constant over the four age groups tested).

Relationships Among Outcome Measures, Year, and Sample Size (Decoding). To the student of meta-analysis, the relationships of the outcome measures to each other and to year and sample size will be important. Table 2 (above diagonal) shows these relationships, expressed in product-moment correlations. From 1923 to 1976, the sample sizes decreased, but effect size and frequency of statistical significance increased, indicating that measurement may have become more reliable and/or more valid to offset the reduced power brought by smaller *N*s. Year was not related to the direction of the effect, indicating that the proportion of studies showing female advantage was more or less constant. As noted earlier, this would lead one to speculate that the larger effect sizes and higher likelihood of statistical significance were not due to real historical changes in men's and women's skill, but rather to the power and precision afforded by more sophisticated methods. Sample size was not related to effect size, which is what one would expect since the effect size index is supposed to be independent of sample size; but sample size was not related to statistical significance, either, which one would not expect. Again, other methodological improvements may account for increases in statistical significance.

The three outcome measures were significantly related to each other, as one would hope. (The statistical significance index does not technically take into account the direction of the effect, but it effectively does, since twenty-three of the twenty-four significant results favored women.) The three outcome measures are far from redundant, though. An investigator would lose information by not including all three.

Analysis by Decade (Decoding). If we examine the data at different points in time, we will be able to judge the ability of a hypothetical reviewer to detect a pattern of gender differences from different historical perspectives. Table 3 shows such a breakdown for the fifty-five visual-cue studies. This group of studies was chosen because visual studies comprised 73 percent of

Table 2. Intercorrelations of Outcome Measures, Year, and Sample Size

	Year	*Sample Size*	*Direction of Effect*[a]	*Effect Size*[b]	*Statistical Significance*[c]
Year	–	–.38[g](72)	.05 (59)	.28[d](44)	.34[f](73)
Sample Size	.43[e](24)	–	.21 (59)	–.07 (44)	.04 (72)
Direction of Effect	.24 (19)	.05 (19)	–	.48[g](42)	.27[e](59)
Effect Size	.36 (18)	–.14 (18)	.66[f](17)	–	.52[g](44)
Statistical Significance	.05 (24)	–.42[e](24)	.33 (19)	.50[e](18)	–

Note: Correlations for decoding studies are above diagonal; correlations for encoding studies are below diagonal. Degrees of freedom are in parentheses.
[a]Coded: 2 = females scored better, 1 = males scored better
[b]Positive values indicate female advantage, negative values indicate male advantage
[c]Coded: 0 = $p > .05$, 1 = $p \leq .05$
[d]$p \leq .10$ (two-tail)
[e]$p \leq .05$ (two-tail)
[f]$p \leq .01$ (two-tail)
[g]$p < .001$ (two-tail)

the entire data set and because most reviewers seemed to be in touch mainly with this part of the literature.

Before the 1940s our reviewer would observe that ten out of ten studies that showed a non-zero gender difference showed female advantage; the mean *d* (based on seven studies) was $.32\sigma$; and 2/16 (12 percent) were significant, both favoring women. Before the 1960s, eighteen of twenty-three studies (78 percent) showed female advantage; the mean *d* was $.18\sigma$ (16 studies); and 4/31 (13 percent) were significant, all favoring women. Clearly the most persuasive research was conducted in the 1970s where all three indices agreed. However, even the earlier hypothetical reviews would have shown significant proportions favoring women; both mean *d*s were almost significantly above zero ($p \leq .06$, two-tail); and the percentages showing statistical significance in favor of women were several times the number that would be expected by chance. Although earlier reviewers would not have known about effect sizes, it seems to me that the pattern should have been detectable on the basis of the other two indices. It is also instructive that the most unsophisticated method is the most reliable and convincing throughout—a simple count of studies going in one direction or the other.

The Encoding Data Set

This data set consists of studies that were published or known to be submitted for publication at the time of the review. As with the decoding data set, the encoding review is based on the same set of twenty-six studies that was

Table 3. Decoding Gender Differences by Decade (Visual Studies Only)

Decade	*Average Sample Size*[a]	*Direction of Effect*[b]	*Effect Size*[c]	*Statistical Significance*[d]
1920s	539(9)	4/4(100%)	.00(1)	0/10(0%)
1930s	384(6)	6/6(100%)	.37(6)	2/6(33%)
1940s	212(9)	6/9(67%)	–.05(4)	0/9(0%)
1950s	153(5)	2/4(50%)	.18(5)	2/5(40%)
1960s	390(1)	1/1(100%)	.11(1)	0/1(0%)
1970s	85(24)	16/18(89%)	.53(12)	8/24(33%)[e]
Summary	227(54)	35/42(83%)	.32(29)	12/55(22%)[f]

[a]*N* of studies is in parentheses
[b]Fraction of studies in which females scored better than males
[c]Positive values indicate female advantage, negative values indicate male advantage; N of studies is in parentheses
[d]Proportion of studies significant at $p \leq .05$ (all favored females except where noted)
[e]One of these favored males significantly
[f]92% of the significant studies favored females

described in earlier papers (Hall, 1977, 1979). Several other studies have come to light since then. Cunningham (1977) and Zuckerman and others (1979) found no gender differences for facial encoding, but Zuckerman and others found that men encoded vocal pleasantness via filtered speech better than women ($-.58\sigma$). Fidell (1977) found that college women posed facial expressions of emotion better than men (4.04σ and 4.07σ using two independent groups of decoders).

To be included, a study had to measure ability to encode nonverbal cues by males and females via facial expression, body movement, or content-free voice tone cues; had to employ the decoding accuracy of a group of decoders as the criterion of encoding accuracy (in most studies the exact same group of decoders judged both male and female senders); and had to report some findings relevant to the encoding accuracy of male versus female encoders. Using these criteria, twenty-six results from twenty-two independent samples of encoders were included in the data set. The *N* of studies used is twenty-six, to maximize stability and power, even though not all are independent. Because such studies were relatively scarce, a study was included even if its encoding group consisted of just one male and one female. Clearly the inclusion of such studies could introduce some error into the data, due to the fact that a single male and a single female encoder could differ on many relevant variables besides gender (acting ability, or facial musculature, for example). Using larger groups of encoders does not solve this problem by any means, since gender remains correlated with other attributes, such as gender-role-related personality characteristics. However, the larger the group of encoders, the less likely is the *complete* confounding of gender with other attributes.

In these studies, groups of judges ranging in size from 2 to over 200 viewed and/or listened to the nonverbal stimuli either "live" or prerecorded on still or movie film, videotape, or audiotape. They were asked to make judgments, multiple-choice or checklist style, of the emotional or other meaning of the expression, of the degree of friendliness in the stimuli, of the truth or falsehood of the vocal expressions, of the pleasantness of the sender's feelings, or of the affective nature of the stimuli that elicited the facial expressions. The first three kinds of dependent variables were employed in studies of "posed" affects, and the last two were employed in studies using "spontaneous" affective displays. In the studies employing spontaneous expressions, the experimenters surreptitiously recorded encoders' faces while they were viewing affectively arousing visual material on slides, videotape, or in person. In all studies, the judgments of the decoding subjects were scored for accuracy and those mean scores, computed separately for each encoder or for each gender of encoder, were the encoding accuracy scores examined in the present study.

For studies using audio nonverbal cues, four methods of masking the verbal content were employed. Three were described earlier: standard-content speech, randomized-spliced speech, and electronically filtered speech. In one study included in the present review, encoders gave answers to personal questions, and decoding subjects had to decide which answers were true and which were false. The verbal content of the statements did, therefore, vary between encoders and between conditions but the authors stated that encoders were instructed to give plausible answers, if lying, so that the content of the answer would not give away the fact that they were lying.

For each study, the following were coded: year, size of encoding group, age of encoding group, channel and medium of expression (for example, vocal cues conveyed via readings of standard verbal content), and modality (posed versus spontaneously occurring). Outcome measures were the same as in the decoding review.

Overall Results for Encoding. Table 1 summarizes the overall encoding results. The conclusion is the same as for decoding—females excel in encoding skill. Because of the smaller number of studies, the significance levels tend sometimes to be less dramatic, but the results are quite similar. The combined overall probability is .0036, one-tail. The average effect size of $.66\sigma$ is larger than that for decoding ($.40\sigma$). Though this invites interpretation, three points should be made. First, males of all ages may be more inhibited in laboratory studies of emotional encoding than are females, and thus the data may underestimate males' actual encoding abilities. Second, the data employed in the decoding summary were probably more unreliable than are the encoding scores, for the following reason. Decoding accuracy scores are based on N of encoders × N of emotions, whereas encoding accuracy scores are based on N of decoders × N of emotions. Since almost all of these studies employ more decoders than encoders, it follows that the average encoder's score is based on more observations than is the average decoder's score and therefore is a more stable score. Larger effect sizes would result from this reduction of measurement error. And third, some of the encoding gender effects were calculated using more powerful tests (such as repeated measures designs) which would tend to produce larger effects (Rosenthal, 1980; Rosenthal and DePaulo, 1979).

In this data set, female advantage was pronounced for visual cues ($d = .88\sigma$) but was nonexistent for auditory cues ($d = .00\sigma$), $t(16) = 1.96$, $p = .067$, two-tail. In the decoding data, female advantage was also greater for visual cues, but not as much so.

Relationships Among Outcome Measures, Year, and Sample Size (Encoding). Table 2 (below diagonal) shows the relationships of the outcome measures to each other and to year and sample size. Unfortunately the total number of studies is much smaller in this data set, making inference more difficult. Nevertheless, the picture is tentatively interpretable in a number of interesting ways.

As the years progressed, the number of subjects (encoders) employed increased, rather than decreased as was the case for decoding studies. Effect sizes also tended to increase (consistent with the decoding summary), but statistical significance did not change (unlike with decoding). Since employing more senders would typically (but not necessarily) lead to more test items, it seems that the evolving methodology consisted of creating more reliable tests (longer, based on more senders), which permitted the use of fewer decoding subjects. Consistent with such a trend, the correlation between N of encoders and N of decoders in the nineteen studies that appear in both reviews is $-.47$ ($p < .05$).

But larger samples here also meant *less* frequent occurrence of statistical significance and slightly decreased size of effect, both of which are unexpected. Improved reliability should increase statistical power and effect sizes by reducing error, and more degrees of freedom should also increase power. Examination of the particular studies magnifies the mystery since several studies with only two senders each (one male, one female) showed some of the larger effects (2.10σ, $.92\sigma$, 2.95σ, 1.41σ), and three of four just named were significant. The explanation of the larger effects and higher frequency of significance among studies with fewer senders is that these studies were more likely to be analyzed using sender sex as a repeated measure factor in a design which used decoders as sampling units; because N of decoders was often large and repeated measures designs are powerful, there was more chance of achieving larger effects and significance when the data were analyzed that way (Rosenthal, 1980; Rosenthal and DePaulo, 1979). These analyses were either performed by the original authors or by this author using data provided in the text. Of the five studies that probably treated sender sex as a within-judges factor, four were significant; of the ten studies that probably treated sender sex as a between-senders factor, only four were significant. This illustrates a potential danger of employing effect size and significance level as measures of outcome in a thoughtless manner: Both are highly sensitive to features of design and analysis. Such procedures are unbiased but, even so, can create a confusing pattern of results for the meta-analyst to deal with. As in the case of decoding, the three outcome measures were positively intercorrelated.

Table 4. **Encoding Gender Differences by Decade (Visual Studies Only)**

Decade	*Average Sample Size*[a]	*Direction of Effect*[b]	*Effect Size*[c]	*Statistical Significance*[d]
1930s	2(1)	–	.00(1)	0/1(0%)
1940s	2(3)	3/3(100%)	1.22(3)	2/3(67%)
1950s	–	–	–	–
1960s	57(4)	1/2(50%)	.22(2)	1/4(25%)
1970s	34(9)	5/7(71%)	1.10(5)	2/9(22%)
Summary	32(17)	9/12(75%)	.88(11)	5/17(29%)[e]

[a]*N* of studies is in parentheses
[b]Fraction of studies in which females scored better than males
[c]Positive values indicate female advantage, negative values indicate male advantage; N of studies is in parentheses
[d]Proportion of studies significant at $p \leq .05$
[e]All of the significant studies favored females

Analysis by Decade (Encoding). As before, a breakdown by decades was made of the seventeen visual studies, which constituted 65 percent of the total number of studies (Table 4). The reviewer at the end of the 1940s or 1950s would have concluded that of the studies that showed any sort of difference, 100 percent favored women; the mean effect size was $.92\sigma$ ($p < .20$, two-tail); and 50 percent of all the studies favored females significantly. Even based on only four studies, this picture is consistent. At the end of the 1960s the reviewer would still see that 80 percent of the studies favored women; the mean effect size was $.68\sigma$ ($p < .13$, two-tail); and 38 percent of all the studies significantly favored women. The cumulative data based on all seventeen studies (through 1977) are most convincing of all, with a mean d of $.88\sigma$ ($p < .001$, two-tail).

Conclusions

The purpose of this chapter was to present meta-analyses of two actual data sets using three measures of outcome. Even if reviewers had been on top of the growing literatures—especially the decoding literature—and had made accurate assessments over the years, doing a careful quantitative review provides information beyond what is learned using the more standard verbal, interpretative review approach. We can examine time trends; how extratheoretical variables such as sample size affect outcome; how theoretical variables, separately and in interaction, influence outcome; and how various outcome measures are related to each other. The present reviews profited a great deal from employing several such indices.

We can also try to determine which outcome indices have done the best job, by showing effects consistently and sensitively. In the case of the decoding literature, the simple and ancient method of counting how many results favor each group, regardless of significance and magnitude, was the most consistent index over the years. For the encoding literature the same argument might be made, but there the superiority of counting is not as clear. As someone who strongly favors using multiple measures, especially effect size, I will not advocate that we revert to our apparently crudest method. I will argue, however, that we should retain this method because its lack of sensitivity is actually a virtue.

Any statistical index of effect size, such as *d,* is affected both by the size of the mean difference and the amount of error variance. The size and direction of the mean difference are likely to be relevant theoretically, but error variance is probably not. However, studies that use more precise and more valid measuring instruments or that reduce extraneous variability by using homogeneous samples will produce larger *d*s. Furthermore, the way in which the data are analyzed influences *d*; more powerful tests and designs employing blocking and repeated measures will yield larger *d*s because extraneous variability is controlled for statistically. Lastly, the reviewer such as myself who computes *d* as best as she can from sometimes minimal published data may make computational errors or errors of judgment. Statistical significance, as another index of outcome, is also influenced by some of the same factors (because it is influenced by effect size) and is also influenced by sample size—another theoretically irrelevant variable. Thus, it is often hard to know what accounts for the size of the effect and for degree of significance.

The direction of the effect, on the other hand, is probably more robust in the face of most of the factors just named. In the extreme case in which measurement is made with an instrument that has no validity and/or no reliability, the direction would tend to be indeterminate or to favor one group when the population difference actually favors the other group. It is likely, however, that a true difference would show up most of the time with this index since it counts a difference even if it is very small. Thus studies with low power could still show a positive result.

Combining results in terms of direction of effect is not the most powerful combining technique available. But the more powerful methods have their own flaws. Aside from the problems of interpreting *d* and *p*, described earlier, methods based on those statistics are greatly limited by the available information. Combining exact probabilities and testing the mean *d* cannot be done effectively, if at all, unless data are originally reported in relatively rigorous ways. Direction of effect, however, is much more likely to be available. Though simple, it has proved to be a very informative and valid outcome measure.

References

Anonymous. "Young Children's Recognition of Nonverbal Communication in the Facial, Vocal, and Gestural Modalities." Unpublished manuscript reviewed by J. A. Hall, 1979.

Brunori, P., Ladavas, E., and Bitti, P. E. R. "Differential Aspects in the Recognition of Facial Expressions of Emotions." Unpublished manuscript, University of Bologna, 1979.

Cohen, J. *Statistical Power Analysis for the Behavioral Sciences.* (rev. ed.) New York: Academic Press, 1977.

Coleman, J. C. "Facial Expressions of Emotion." *Psychological Monographs,* 1949, *63* (1, whole no. 296).

Cunningham, M. R. "Personality and the Structure of the Nonverbal Communication of Emotion." *Journal of Personality,* 1977, *45,* 564–584.

Daly, E. M., Abramovitch, R., and Pliner, P. "The Relationship Between Mothers' Encoding and Their Children's Decoding of Facial Expressions of Emotion." Unpublished manuscript, University of Toronto, 1979.

Davitz, J. R. "A Review of Research Concerned with Facial and Vocal Expressions of Emotion." In J. R. Davitz (Ed.), *The Communication of Emotional Meaning.* New York: McGraw-Hill, 1964.

Davitz, J. R., and Davitz, L. "Correlates of Accuracy in the Communication of Feelings." *Journal of Communication,* 1959, *9,* 110–117.

Feldman, M., and Thayer, S. "A Comparison of Three Measures of Nonverbal Decoding Ability." Unpublished manuscript, South Beach Psychiatric Center, Staten Island, N.Y., 1978.

Fidell, L. E. "The Development of the Facial Assessment of Communicated Emotion Test (the FACE Test) and Its Use in a Training Session in Nonverbal Sensitivity." Unpublished honors thesis, Harvard University, 1977.

Friedman, H. "Magnitude of Experimental Effect and a Table for Its Rapid Estimation." *Psychological Bulletin,* 1968, *70,* 245–251.

Gitter, A. G., Kozel, N. J., and Mostofsky, D. I. "Perception of Emotion: The Role of Race, Sex, and Presentation Mode." *Journal of Social Psychology,* 1972, *88,* 213–222.

Hall, J. A. "Gender Effects in Encoding Nonverbal Cues." Unpublished manuscript, The Johns Hopkins University, 1977.

Hall, J. A. "Gender Effects in Decoding Nonverbal Cues." *Psychological Bulletin,* 1978, *85,* 845–857.

Hall, J. A. "Gender, Gender Roles, and Nonverbal Communication Skill." In R. Rosenthal (Ed.), *Skill in Nonverbal Communication: Individual Differences.* Cambridge, Mass.: Oelgeschlager, Gunn, and Hain, 1979.

Hoffman, M. L. "Sex Differences in Empathy and Related Behaviors." *Psychological Bulletin,* 1977, *84,* 712–722.

Jenness, A. "The Recognition of Facial Expressions of Emotion." *Psychological Bulletin,* 1932, *29,* 324–350.

Maccoby, E. E., and Jacklin, C. N. *The Psychology of Sex Differences.* Stanford, Calif.: Stanford University Press, 1974.

Rogers, P. L., Scherer, K. R., and Rosenthal, R. "Content Filtering Human Speech: A Simple Electronic System." *Behavior Research Methods and Instrumentation,* 1971, *3,* 16–18.

Rosenthal, R. "Combining Results of Independent Studies." *Psychological Bulletin,* 1978, *85,* 185–193.

Rosenthal, R. "The 'File Drawer Problem' and Tolerance for Null Results." *Psychological Bulletin,* 1979, *86,* 638–641.

Rosenthal, R. "Conducting Judgment Studies." In K. R. Scherer and P. Ekman (Eds.), *Methods of Research in Nonverbal Communication.* Submitted for Publication, 1980.

Rosenthal, R., and DePaulo, B. M. "Encoders Versus Decoders as Units of Analysis in Research in Nonverbal Communication." Unpublished manuscript, Harvard University, 1979.

Rosenthal, R., Hall, J. A., DiMatteo, M. R., Rogers, P. L., and Archer, D. *Sensitivity to Nonverbal Communication: The PONS Test.* Baltimore: Johns Hopkins University Press, 1979.

Scherer, K. R. "Randomized Splicing: A Note on a Simple Technique for Masking Speech Content." *Journal of Experimental Research in Personality,* 1971, *5,* 155–159.

Tagiuri, R. "Person Perception." In G. Lindzey and E. Aronson (Eds.), *Handbook of Social Psychology.* (2nd ed.) Vol. 3. Reading, Mass.: Addison-Wesley, 1969.

Weisgerber, C. A. "Accuracy in Judging Emotional Expressions as Related to College Entrance Test Scores." *Journal of Social Psychology,* 1956, *44,* 233–239.

West, L. "Women's Intuition: An Interdisciplinary Analysis." Unpublished master's thesis, George Washington University, 1979.

Zuckerman, M., Larrance, D. T., Hall, J. A., DeFrank, R. S., and Rosenthal, R. "Posed and Spontaneous Communication of Emotion via Facial and Vocal Cues." *Journal of Personality,* 1979, *47,* 712–733.

Judith A. Hall received her B.A. and Ph.D. degrees from Harvard University and has held positions at Johns Hopkins University and at Harvard University. Her main interest is in nonverbal communication, especially gender differences.

Expectancy effects are manifested in well-controlled studies, the average size varying with the research area.

Summarizing 345 Studies of Interpersonal Expectancy Effects

Robert Rosenthal
Donald B. Rubin

There is a large and growing number of experiments investigating the hypothesis that person A's expectation for person B's behavior can affect B's behavior in such a way as to increase the probability that B will behave as expected. These interpersonal self-fulfilling prophecies have been found to operate in psychological experiments in such a way that behavioral researchers are more likely to obtain the results they expect to obtain solely because they expect those results (Rosenthal, 1966, 1976). These interpersonal self-fulfilling prophecies have also been found to operate in classrooms and workshops in such a way that teachers and supervisors are more likely to obtain the performances they expect to obtain solely because they expect those performances (Rosenthal, 1973).

The pervasive effects of interpersonal expectations are of special importance both scientifically and socially. They are important scientifically because there is a possibility that many studies in the behavioral and medical

Preparation of this chapter was supported in part by the National Science Foundation. It is based on a more detailed exposition by the same authors in *The Behavioral and Brain Sciences,* 1978, *3,* 377–415.

sciences have obtained their results partially because of the particular hypothesis or expectation held by the researchers. They are important socially because pupils' or employees' performances may be lowered because teachers or employers expect performance to be low. When behavioral researchers, teachers, or supervisors expect a certain level of performance from their subjects, pupils, or supervisees, they appear unwittingly to treat them in such a way so as to increase the probability that they will respond as they are expected to respond.

Because these experiments hold special scientific and social importance, they have been closely examined by critics who have tried to show that one or more or even all of these studies were deficient in one or more crucial ways (for example, Barber, 1976; Barber and Silver, 1968; Elashoff and Snow, 1970, 1971; Jensen, 1969; Thorndike, 1968). These criticisms have been answered elsewhere (for example, Rosenthal, 1968, 1969a, 1969b, 1973, 1976; Rosenthal and Rubin, 1971, 1978). In this chapter the intent is not to focus on the good studies or the bad studies, the likeable results or the unlikeable results, the big effects or the small effects; rather the intent is to focus on the results of *all* the studies that could be found that have investigated the effects of the interpersonal self-fulfilling prophecy.

In this chapter the results of 345 studies will be addressed and summarized and it will be shown that: (1) the overall probability that there is no such thing as interpersonal expectancy effects is near zero; and (2) the average magnitude of the effect of interpersonal expectations is likely to be of practical importance. In the course of summarizing the results of all available studies, methods will be illustrated that will be of use to others wanting to summarize quantitatively entire areas of research, including combining probabilities, estimating effect sizes, placing confidence intervals around these estimates, and systematically addressing various issues of data accessibility, quality, and retrievability.

The structure of the chapter is as follows. After some typical experiments are described, statistical significance is considered for each of eight areas of research that have been investigated. Then we consider the average size of the effects of interpersonal expectations for each of the eight areas of research and for all eight together. Issues of quality control are discussed and attention is given to problems of unretrieved studies, sampling, minimal quality of data, and controls for cheating and recording errors. Practical implications discussed include (1) the degree to which interpersonal expectations function in everyday life situations as well as in laboratories and (2) the degree to which the magnitude of experimenter expectancy effects are as large as other variables of psychological importance such as brain lesions, preparatory effort, and persuasive communications. Finally, our conclusions include an overview of the types of future research suggested by our analyses.

Some Sample Studies

Before beginning our summary it will be useful to illustrate the type of experiment that has been conducted on interpersonal expectancy effects both in the laboratory and in everyday life situations.

Two Animal Experiments. Twelve experimenters were each given five rats. The rats were to be taught to run a maze with the aid of visual cues. Half the experimenters were told that their rats had been specially bred for maze-brightness; half the experimenters were told their rats had been bred for maze-dullness. Actually, the rats had been randomly assigned to each of the two groups of experimenters. At the end of the experiment, the results were clear. Rats who had been run by experimenters expecting brighter behavior showed significantly superior learning compared to rats run by experimenters expecting dull behavior (Rosenthal and Fode, 1963). The experiment was repeated, this time employing a series of learning experiments conducted in Skinner boxes. Half the experimenters were led to believe their rats were "Skinner box bright" and half were led to believe their animals were "Skinner box dull." Once again the rats were randomly divided into two groups. But by the end of the experiment, the allegedly brighter animals performed significantly more brightly than did the allegedly duller animals (Rosenthal and Lawson, 1964).

If rats became more bright when expected to by their experimenter, it seemed possible that children might become more bright when expected to by their teacher. Educational theorists had, after all, been saying for a long time that some children were unable to learn because their teachers expected them to be unable to learn. True, there was no experimental evidence for that theory, but the two studies employing rats and similar studies employing humans suggested that these theorists might be correct. The following experiment was therefore conducted (Rosenthal and Jacobson, 1968).

The Pygmalion Experiment. All of the children in an elementary school were administered a nonverbal test of intelligence, which was disguised as a test that would predict intellectual "blooming." There were eighteen classrooms in the school, three at each of the six grade levels. Within each grade level the three classrooms were composed of children with above average ability, average ability, and below average ability, respectively. Within each of the eighteen classrooms approximately 20 percent of the children were chosen at random to form the experimental group. Each teacher was given the names of the children from her class who were in the experimental condition, and told that these children had scores on the "test for intellectual blooming" indicating that they would show remarkable gains in intellectual competence during the next eight months of school. The only systematic difference between the experimental group and the control group children, then, was in the mind of the teacher.

At the end of the school year, eight months later, all the children were retested with the same IQ test. Considering the school as a whole, those children from whom the teachers had been led to expect greater intellectual gains showed significantly greater gains in IQ than did the children of the control group.

Statistical Significance

Our first analyses consider the statistical significance of the results. These analyses could be performed for all 345 of the studies that could be found at the time of writing because all studies provided at least some information about statistical significance, minimally, whether the results reached the .05 level. Table 1 summarizes the significance levels of all 345 studies. The first column gives the total number of studies that fall into each of the eight research areas. The second column of Table 1 shows, for each area, the typical number of degrees of freedom for the two groups being compared in each study. Typical values were calculated by squaring the unbiased estimate of the mean $\sqrt{df}$. The typical *df*s range over the eight research areas from 17 to 97 with a median of 37.

The third column of Table 1 shows the proportion of studies reaching the .05 level of significance in the predicted direction. The range of these proportions was from .22 to .73 with a median proportion of .39. Treating these 350 studies as a sample, these eight proportions differ significantly from each other ($\chi^2(7) = 16.32$, $p = .025$). Inspection of the squared differences between the expected and obtained frequencies divided by the expected frequencies, showed that only two research areas were contributing substantially to the large obtained χ^2. The area of animal learning showed more significant effects than did the other seven areas combined, $\chi^2(1) = 8.02$, $p = .005$, while the area of person perception showed fewer significant effects than did the other seven areas combined, $\chi^2(1) = 5.54$, $p = .02$. The difference in frequency with which these two areas yielded significant expectancy effects was not due to differences in size of the samples employed in these two areas; indeed, the area showing fewer significant effects had employed larger sample sizes. For the present, we simply conclude that studies of animal learning are more likely to yield significant effects of experimenter expectation than other areas of research while studies of person perception are less likely to yield significant effects.

Table 1. Significance of Expectancy Effects in Eight Research Areas

Research Area	*Number of Studies*	*Estimated Typical df*[b]	*Proportion of Studies Reaching p<.05*	*Approximated Z Standard Normal Deviate*
Reaction Time	9	94	.22[c]	+2.14
Inkblot Tests	9	25	.44[c]	+4.05
Animal Learning	15	17	.73[c]	+7.73
Laboratory Interviews	29	37	.38[c]	+6.71
Psychophysical Judgments	23	25	.43[c]	+6.61
Learning and Ability	34	39	.29[c]	+5.14
Person Perception	119	37	.27[c]	+6.62
Everyday Situations	112	97	.40[c]	+14.24
Median	26[a]	37	.39	6.62

[a]Five entries occur in more than one area
[b]Calculated from the sample of 113 studies in Table 2 by finding the unbiased estimate of $\sqrt{df}$ and then squaring.
[c]The proportions in this column differ significantly from each other $\chi^2 = 16.32$, $df = 7$, $p = .025$

The final column of Table 1 shows the standard normal deviates of the combined results for all studies in each area. In order to be consistent with the procedure of an earlier review (Rosenthal, 1969b), however, any Z falling between -1.27 and $+1.27$ was entered as zero, a procedure used because of the paucity of information in many studies claiming non-significant results. It is expected that this procedure leads to combined results that are too conservative in the long run. The results shown in this final column also show significant overall effects of interpersonal expectancies in all research areas.

Effect Size

So far we have examined only the significance levels of our studies. Unfortunately, in most of the studies examined only significance levels and perhaps sample size and a test statistic were reported. But to know the p level is not to know enough about the results of a study. Increasingly, behavioral researchers are asking to know about the magnitude of the effects of the treatments being studied (Cohen, 1969, 1977).

Cohen's *d*. The primary index of effect size employed in the present chapter is the statistic d defined as the difference between the means of the two groups being compared, divided by the within-group standard deviation assumed common to the two populations (Cohen, 1969, p. 18; 1977, p. 20). This index is useful because it permits us to compare the magnitudes of effects for a large variety of measures. It frees us from the particular scale of measurement used in a study and allows us to speak of effects measured in standard deviation units. This property is a great advantage in the behavioral sciences where responses are measured on many different scales having varying means and standard deviations. Although there are other measures of effect size (see, for example, the chapters by Glass and by Smith in this volume) d was chosen both for its simplicity and because it appears especially appropriate given that a large proportion of the studies of interpersonal expectancy effects involve simply a comparison of an experimental with a control group by means of a t test; d is particularly useful for that situation because it is conceptually appropriate and computationally convenient. (For a recent example of the extensive use of d as an index of effect size in the behavioral sciences, see Rosenthal and Rosnow, 1975.)

Sampling Procedures. Suppose, first, that we had the results of all 345 studies. For many purposes we would want to think of these as a sample from a population of similar studies that could have been done in the past or might be done in the future. Consequently, even though we could not find any more studies to date, we would have made the usual types of inferences, for example, about effect sizes from our 345 studies to the hypothetical target population. In fact, the test statistics previously calculated from Table 1 refer to this hypothetical target population.

Although it would have been possible to go back to our 345 studies of interpersonal expectations and to compute for each one the effect size, a stratified probability sample of 113 studies was chosen to permit the estimation of effect sizes. Two stratification variables were used: area of research and statistical significance of the results. The first three columns of Table 2 present the sampling scheme. For the two areas of research with fewer than ten studies, reaction time and inkblot tests, all studies were included. For the remaining six areas, fifteen studies were included for each area except for the area of everyday situations for which twenty studies were included. These studies were chosen as follows: the five most significant studies were included for each area except for the area of everyday situations for which the ten most significant studies were included, and ten studies were selected at random from the remaining studies in each area.

This stratification increases the precision of estimated effect size since effect size is usually correlated with level of significance when sample sizes tend to be homogeneous across studies. For summary purposes, the mean effect size in each area was estimated and is given in the fourth column of Table 2. For example, there were thirty-four studies of the effects of experimenter expectations on the learning and ability scores of their subjects. The mean effect size (as measured by Cohen's *d*) of the five most significant studies was 1.25. The mean effect size of the ten studies randomly selected from the remaining twenty-nine studies was 0.42. The estimated effect size for all thirty-four studies was 0.54, a value much closer to the mean of the ten studies than to the mean of the highly significant five studies. The means are weighted by 5 and N – 5, respectively, so that the overall estimated effect size is given by $[5\,\overline{X}\text{ high} + (N-5)\,\overline{X}\text{ random}]/N$, where N is the total number of studies conducted in that area.

Estimates for the Eight Research Areas. The range of estimated effect sizes is from 0.14 for studies of laboratory interviews to 1.73 for studies of animal learning, with a median effect size of 0.70. In Cohen's (1969, p. 38) terminology, then, these effect sizes range from small (.20) through medium (.50) to large (.80) and, for two of the research areas, to very large. As anticipated by the sampling procedure, there was a large correlation (.88) between the estimated effect size (Table 2) and the proportion of studies (Table 1) reaching significance across the eight areas of research.

In order to obtain a better understanding of the probable range of effect sizes for the various areas of research, confidence intervals were computed and these are shown in columns six and seven of Table 2. For each area of research, the 95 percent confidence interval suggests the likely range of the effect size for that area. If we claim that the effect size falls within the range given we will be correct 95 percent of the time. The confidence intervals are wide because their computation was based on such small samples of studies (that is, 9, 15, or 20) and most of them overlap substantially. However, the confidence interval for reaction time is below the confidence intervals for animal learning and psychophysical judgments, and the confidence interval for laboratory interviews is below the confidence interval for animal learning. Studies of reaction time appear to have a particularly narrow confidence interval, and a test for the equality of standard errors is consistent with that view; $F\,\max = 93.4$; $p < .01$.

Table 2. Results of Sampling from 345 Studies in Eight Research Areas

Research Area	*Number of Studies Sampled* n_{high}	n_{random}	n_{total}	*Mean Effect Size*	*Standard Error of the Mean (SE)*	*95% Confidence Interval* *From*	*To*	*Correlation Between Effect Size and Level of Significance (z)*[d]
Reaction Time	—	—	9	0.17	.06[a]	+0.03	0.31	.91
Inkblot Tests	—	—	9	0.84	.39[a]	−0.06	1.74	.85
Animal Learning	5	10	15	1.73	.35[b]	+0.97	2.49	.69
Laboratory Interviews	5	10	15	0.14	.23[b]	−0.36	0.64	.89
Psychophysical Judgments	5	10	15	1.05	.26[b]	+0.49	1.61	.62
Learning and Ability	5	10	15	0.54	.31[b]	−0.13	1.21	.66
Person Perception	5	10	15	0.55	.21[b]	+0.10	1.00	.69
Everyday Situations	10	10	20	0.88	.58[b]	−0.34	2.10	.46
Median				0.70	.28	−0.02	1.41	.69
Estimated Mean of 345 Studies				0.70	.20[c]	0.30	1.10	

[a]Computed as $\sqrt{\frac{S^2_{total}}{n}}$

[b]Computed as $\sqrt{\left(\frac{n_{high}}{N}\right)^2\left(\frac{S^2_{high}}{n_{high}}\right)+\left(\frac{N-n_{high}}{N}\right)^2\left(\frac{S^2_{random}}{10}\right)}$ where N = total number of studies in that area (Column 1 of Table 1)

[c]Computed as $\sqrt{\sum_{i=1}^{8}\left(\frac{N_i}{N}\right)^2(SE_i)^2}$ where N_i is the number of studies available in area i (Column 1 of Table 1), $N = \sum_{i=1}^{8} N_i = 350$, and SE_i is given above

[d]Computed from unbiased estimates of the average value of d, d^2, Z, Z^2, and dZ

When we consider all 113 studies sampled, we find that the 95 percent confidence interval suggests an average overall effect size between 0,30 and 1.10 corresponding to effect magnitudes ranging from small/medium to quite large in the spirit of Cohen's (1969) terminology. The last column of Table 2 reports estimated correlations obtained within each research area between the effect size and the degree of statistical significance measured in standard normal deviates. These correlations were all positive ranging from + .46 to + .91 with a median correlation of + .69. We would expect high correlations in research areas employing relatively homogeneous sample sizes.

Issues of Quality Control

On the basis of the 345 studies, we have shown that interpersonal expectancy effects are real in the sense of statistical significance and are at least moderate in average magnitude. In this section we address the questions of whether these conclusions about interpersonal expectancy effects might reasonably be attributed to problems of sampling or of data quality. We proceed in four sections.

1. *The File Drawer Analysis.* In this section we show that it is unreasonable to suppose that there exist enough unpublished nonsignificant studies to overwhelm the studies we have considered.

2. *Dissertation Data.* Doctoral dissertations are more readily retrievable, less likely to be suppressed because of nonsignificant results, and more likely to meet at least minimum standards of quality. Yet doctoral dissertations show expectancy effects that are statistically significant as well as at least moderate in magnitude.

3. *Controls for Cheating and Recording Error.* Those studies instituting special safeguards against intentional or recording errors exhibit interpersonal expectancy effects that are significant statistically and at least moderate in magnitude.

4. *Dissertations with Special Controls.* In this section we consider those studies that have special controls for cheating and recording errors and are also doctoral dissertations and therefore especially retrievable and likely to satisfy at least minimum standards of quality. These studies also exhibit effects of interpersonal expectancy that are significant statistically and at least moderate in size.

The File Drawer Analysis. In our overview of research on interpersonal expectations, the results of 345 independent studies were summarized. These studies were all the ones we could locate employing the usual formal and informal bibliographic search procedures. *Psychological Abstracts, Dissertation Abstracts International,* programs of conventions of national and regional psychological, sociological, and educational conferences, various computer assisted searches, and word of mouth were all employed to maximize the chances of finding all studies of interpersonal expectancy effects. Nevertheless, it was possible that many studies could not be retrieved because they were regarded by their authors as uninteresting or counter-intuitive, or overly complex, or whatever. Such studies may have shown preponderantly negative results. Could it be that there are enough unretrieved studies to make our combined results not significant? The sum of the standard normal deviates associated with the significance levels of our 345 studies was about +421. We would have to retrieve 65,122 studies with a mean standard normal deviate of zero in order to lower the overall combined standard normal deviate to +1.645 ($p = .05$). It certainly seems unlikely that there are file drawers crammed with the unpublished results of over 65,000 studies of interpersonal expectations (Rosenthal, 1979a)!

Dissertation Data. Although sampling bias cannot reasonably explain the overall significant results of studies of interpersonal expectancies, the studies that could be found might still differ in various ways from the studies that could not be found. It would be quite useful to examine a class of study for which we could be more sure of having found all the research performed, even if the class is not representative of all classes of studies. Such an opportunity exists to some extent in the case of doctoral dissertations. If the dissertation is accepted by the university where it is conducted it usually can be retrieved through *Dissertation Abstracts International* (DAI). Dissertation work not accepted because the results are "nonsignificant" (see Rosenthal, 1966, p. 366) or in a direction displeasing to one or more members of the student's committee will, of course, not be retrievable.

Another reason for examining dissertation data more closely was that dissertations usually satisfy at least minimum standards of quality of design and analysis since a doctoral committee usually approves the plan before it is undertaken and approves the analysis and report after it is completed.

Table 3 compares the sample of 32 dissertations with the sample of 81 non-dissertations with respect to size of effect and statistical significance of the results. The first two columns show the number of studies in each research area that were dissertations or non-dissertations; 32 percent of the 345 studies were doctoral dissertations while 28 percent of the 113 studies sampled were doctoral dissertations.

The third column of Table 3 gives the estimated overall mean effect size (d) for each area while columns four and five give the estimated effect sizes separately for the dissertations and non-dissertations. The sixth column shows the differences between the estimated effect sizes for dissertations and non-dissertations. These differences ranged from −1.19 favoring the dissertations to +1.38 favoring the non-dissertations, with a median difference of +.35 favoring the non-dissertations. Thus dissertations tended to show smaller effect sizes than did non-dissertations.

The seventh column of Table 3 gives the estimated overall mean standard normal deviate (Z) for each research area while the next two columns give estimated mean Zs separately for dissertations and non-dissertations. The last column shows the differences between the Zs estimated for dissertations

Table 3. Mean Effect Sizes and Standard Normal Deviates for Dissertations and Non-Dissertations

Research Area	Number of Studies		Mean Effect Sizes				Mean Standard Normal Deviates			
	Dissertations	Non-Dissertations	Total	Dissertations	Non-Dissertations	Difference	Total	Dissertations	Non-Dissertations	Difference
Reaction Time	3	6	0.17	0.21	0.15	−0.06	0.89	0.89	0.89	+0.00
Inkblot Tests	3	6	0.84	0.53	1.00	+0.47	1.41	1.18	1.53	+0.35
Animal Learning	1	14	1.73	0.44	1.82	+1.38	2.10	0.51	2.22	+1.71
Laboratory Interviews	4	11	0.14	−0.03	0.20	+0.23	0.68	0.80	0.66	−0.14
Psychophysical Judgments	2	13	1.05	2.08	0.89	−1.19	1.60	2.66	1.50	−1.16
Learning and Ability	5	10	0.54	0.11	0.76	+0.65	0.82	0.05	0.95	+0.90
Person Perception	5	10	0.55	0.52	0.56	+0.04	0.64	0.75	0.64	−0.11
Everyday Situations	9	11	0.88	0.31	1.35	+1.04	1.03	0.62	1.07	+0.45
Median	3.5	10.5	0.70	0.38	0.82	+0.35	0.96	0.78	1.01	+0.18

and non-dissertations. These differences ranged from − 1.16 favoring the dissertations to + 1.71 favoring the non-dissertations, with a median difference of + .18 favoring the non-dissertations. Thus dissertations tended to show somewhat less statistical significance than did non-dissertations.

The tendency for dissertations to show somewhat smaller effect sizes and less statistical significance might be due to a reduction in sampling bias in retrieving dissertations as compared to non-dissertations, or it might be due to real differences between non-dissertation research and dissertation research (for instance, younger, less prestigious, and less skilled investigators usually perform the latter). A potentially powerful factor might be introduced by dissertation researchers if they were unusually procedure-conscious in the conduct of their research; there are indications that such researchers may tend to obtain data that are biased in the direction *opposite* to their expectations (Rosenthal, 1969b, p. 234).

Controls for Cheating and Recording Errors. Previous work has shown that although the occurrence of cheating or recording errors on the part of experimenters and teachers cannot be definitively ruled out, the occurrence of such intentional or unintentional errors cannot reasonably account for the overall obtained effects of interpersonal expectations (Rosenthal, 1969b, pp. 245–249; 1978). Experiments described there showed major effects of interpersonal expectations despite the impossibility of the occurrence of either cheating or recording errors.

Further evidence for this position is obtained from some special studies. Among the 345 studies under review here, forty-three employed special methods for the elimination or control of cheating or observer errors or permitted an assessment of the possibility of intentional or unintentional errors. These methods included using tape recorded instructions, data recording by observers blind to the treatments, and video-taping of the interaction between the subject and the data-collector. The results of these forty-three studies employing such safeguards were of special interest because if cheating and recording errors really played a major role in "explaining" interpersonal expectancy effects, then we would expect that studies guarding against such errors would show markedly reduced effects of interpersonal expectation.

The mean effect size of the studies employing special controls was .64, a value very close to that estimated for the remaining studies that did not employ such special controls (.71). The difference between these estimated effect sizes occupies only 9 percent of the 95 percent confidence interval around the estimated mean effect size for all 345 studies.

Fifty-six percent of these special 43 studies reached the .05 level of significance in the predicted direction whereas only 33 percent of the remaining 302 studies reached the .05 level of significance in the predicted direction. The results are unequivocal. The more carefully controlled studies are *more* likely ($p = .007$) than the studies permitting at least the possibility of cheating and/or recording errors to show effects of interpersonal expectations significant at $p < .05$. The mean standard normal deviate for the specially controlled studies was + 1.70 whereas that for the remaining studies was + 1.15. The 95 percent confidence interval for the mean of the specially controlled studies was 1.09 to 2.31, and clearly indicates that the forty-three carefully controlled studies did not yield less significant results than the remaining 302 studies. The reason why these especially controlled studies might be more likely than the remaining studies to yield significant effects is not obvious. The median sample size employed in these studies was about the same as the median sample size employed in all 345 studies. Perhaps those investigators careful enough to institute special safeguards against cheating and/or observer errors are also careful enough to reduce nonsystematic errors to a minimum, thereby increasing the precision and power of their experiments.

Dissertations with Special Controls. A subgroup of the forty-three specially controlled studies was of special interest: the eighteen that were also doctoral dissertations. Examination of the results of these studies might permit a reasonable estimate of the results obtained in studies that were both error controlled and less susceptible to sampling bias. Presumably, this group of specially controlled dissertations represents the work of careful dissertation researchers and/or dissertation researchers whose committee members were careful.

The mean effect size of these specially controlled dissertations ($d = 0.78$) was larger than found for the thirty-two dissertations examined in Table 3 ($d = 0.40$); (that set of dissertations includes some of the eighteen dissertations under discussion). The 95 percent confidence interval around the mean effect size for these eighteen runs from 0.26 to + 1.30, or from small to very large, and covers the 95 percent confidence interval calculated from the 113 studies of Table 2 (0.30, 1.10) as well as the 95 percent confidence interval calculated from the forty-three studies employing special controls for cheating and observer errors (.32, .96). There is thus no evidence to suggest that research studies having better controls and greater retrievability are associated with smaller effects of interpersonal expectations.

The mean Z is greater for these specially controlled dissertations ($Z = 1.86$) than for the full set of dissertations examined in Table 3 or for the 345 studies ($Z = 1.22$). The 95 percent confidence interval around the mean level of significance (Z) for the special dissertations ranged from + .93 to + 2.79. The evidence seems quite clear: when we examine specifically those studies that are more precisely retrievable and more precisely controlled, we find no decrease in either the average size of the effect obtained or in the average level of statistical significance.

Practical Implications

In this section we address the practical implications of interpersonal expectations. First, we consider the generality of interpersonal self-fulfilling prophecies when moving from the laboratory to everyday life situations. Then we consider measuring the importance of expectancy effects by comparing their size to the size of the effects of such other important independent variables as brain lesions, preparatory effort, and persuasive communications.

The External Validity of Interpersonal Expectancy Effects. Although many studies of teacher expectation effects have been conducted since the Pygmalion Experiment (Rosenthal, 1973), the majority of the 345 studies surveyed in this chapter have been studies of interpersonal expectation effects in laboratory situations rather than in such everyday situations as schools, clinics, or industries. A simple way to examine the external validity, or generality, of the interpersonal expectancy effect is to compare the results of studies conducted in laboratories with studies conducted in more "real life" situations. (We define laboratories here to include all categories other than everyday situations.)

Such comparisons have been made implicitly in earlier tables. The data from Table 2 imply that the mean effect (d) for everyday situations is 0.88 with a 95 percent confidence interval of $(-0.34, +2.10)$ and the mean effect for laboratory situations is 0.62 with a 95 percent confidence interval of $(+0.38, +0.86)$. Thus effect sizes may tend to be larger, on the average, in everyday situations than in laboratory situations. However, they also appear somewhat more variable; the estimates of standard deviation are 1.90 and 1.52 respectively.

A final comparison is of the proportion of studies reaching the .05 level of significance in the predicted direction for studies conducted in laboratory and everyday situations. The proportions are similar for the two types of studies, studies conducted in everyday situations showing significant results in the predicted direction somewhat more often (.40 versus .34). This is not surprising, since the typical *df* for studies in everyday situations is substantially larger than for other studies, 97 *df* versus 36 *df*.

Consequently, the overall results summarized here support the conclusion that interpersonal expectancy effects are as likely to occur in everyday life situations as in laboratory situations.

Expectancy Control Group Designs. Although we have shown that the average effects of interpersonal expectations are both significant statistically and of moderate to large magnitude, it is also of interest to compare the typical statistical significance and effect size of interpersonal expectations with the typical statistical significance and effect size of other variables studied by psychologists. If it could be shown, for example, that the effects of experimenter expectations were substantially smaller than the effects of some other behavioral research variables, we might decide that experimenter expectancy effects, though real, are not large enough, relative to other behavioral variables, to pose a real threat to the internal validity of our experiments. A particular research paradigm has been developed to compare directly the size of the effect of experimenter expectations and some other variable of greater intrinsic research interest.

This paradigm, the expectancy control group design, has been described in detail elsewhere (Rosenthal, 1966) in the spirit of a form of calibration whereby the effect size of an "artifact" variable can be compared with the effect size of some variable of primary interest. This earlier treatment was exclusively theoretical in the sense that there were no studies available that had employed the suggested paradigm. Now, however, there are five studies available that permit a direct comparison of the effects of experimenter expectancy with such other psychological effects as brain lesions, preparatory efforts, and persuasive communications (Rosenthal and Rubin, 1978).

Table 4 summarizes the results of the five studies by Burnham, by Cooper and others, and by Miller. For each study, the effect size and *Z* are reported for experimenter expectancy as well as for the other variable against which expectancy effects were to be compared. The final rows of Table 4 indicate that the magnitude of expectancy effects were nearly identical to those of the other variables, and that the *Z*s for expectancy effects were slightly more significant than the *Z*s for the other variables.

Five studies are not very many upon which to base any but the most tentative conclusions. Nevertheless, it does appear that there is no evidence to support the idea that the effects of experimenter expectations are small relative to the effects of "real" psychological variables.

Conclusion

We have examined the results of 345 studies of interpersonal self-fulfilling prophecies and some clear conclusions have emerged. The reality of the phenomenon is beyond doubt and the mean size of the effect is clearly not trivial. Depending on the area of research considered, the mean size of the effect varies from small for studies of reaction time and laboratory interviews (*d*s = .17 and .14) to very large for studies of psychophysical judgments and animal learning (*d*s = 1.05 and 1.73). The estimated grand mean effect size over eight different areas of research was .70. This grand mean effect size may also be interpreted in terms of a change in the accuracy of prediction attributable to

Table 4. Summary of Five Experiments Employing Expectancy Control Group Designs

		Effect Size			*Standard Normal Deviate (Z)*		
Study	*df*	*Experimenter Expectancy*	*Other Variable*	*Difference*	*Experimenter Expectancy*	*Other Variable*	*Difference*
Burnham (1966)	21	1.02	.79[a]	−.23	2.05	1.64	−.41
Cooper and others (1967)	96	.71	.07[b]	−.64	3.35	0.33	−3.02
Miller (1970a)	76	.36	1.22[c]	.86	1.56	4.80	3.24
Miller (1970b)	76	.82	.45[c]	−.37	3.40	1.94	−1.46
Miller (1970c)	76	.62	.93[c]	.31	2.62	3.80	1.18
Median		0.71	0.79	−0.23	2.62	1.94	−0.41
Unweighted Mean		0.71	0.69	−0.01	2.60	2.50	−0.09

[a]Brain lesions
[b]Belief as a function of preparatory effort
[c]Persuasive communications

our knowledge of the exposure to the experimental manipulation of interpersonal self-fulfilling prophecies. With $d = .70$, our increase in accuracy would be from 33.5 percent correct to 66.5 percent correct (Rosenthal and Rubin, 1980).

We also considered various issues of quality control. In one analysis we showed that it was unreasonable to suppose that there existed enough unretrieved nonsignificant studies to overwhelm the studies we were able to retrieve. In another analysis we showed that doctoral dissertations which were systematically more retrievable than other unpublished studies also showed statistically significant effects with nontrivial magnitudes. A third analysis showed that studies instituting special safeguards against intentional or recording errors also showed statistically significant effects with nontrivial magnitudes. Finally, we found that for the subset of studies that were doctoral dissertations and especially controlled for intentional and recording errors, the statistical significance and the average magnitudes of effect obtained were as large as for the remainder of the studies.

When we considered the practical implications of our results we showed that the effects of interpersonal expectations were as great, on the average, in everyday life situations as they were in laboratory experiments. We also referred to studies showing that the magnitude of the effects of experimenter expectations were about the same size as the effects of such other important variables as brain lesions, preparation for an examination, and persuasive communications.

Future research suggested by the results of our analyses is of two kinds: that specific to the content of our analyses—the interpersonal self-fulfilling prophecy—and that specific not to our content but to our methods. Future research on self-fulfilling prophecies should (1) explore further the procedures suggested for minimizing and calibrating the effects of experimenter expectations (Rosenthal, 1966, 1976); (2) explore further the interpersonal and policy implications of self-fulfilling prophecies in classrooms, clinics, and businesses (Rosenthal, 1973, 1976); and (3) explore further the role of nonverbal processes of communication serving to mediate interpersonal expectancy effects (Rosenthal, 1979b; Rosenthal, Hall, DiMatteo, Rogers, and Archer, 1979). Finally, future research suggested by our analyses and those of the authors of the other chapters of this volume, but not specific to the present contents, should address the improvement of methods of summarizing entire domains of research with respect to statistical significance, size of effect, and problems of quality control.

References

Barber, T. X. *Pitfalls in Human Research: Ten Pivotal Points.* New York: Pergamon Press, 1976.

Barber, T. X., and Silver, M. J. "Fact, Fiction, and the Experimenter Bias Effect." *Psychological Bulletin Monograph Supplement,* 1968, *70,* 1–29.

Burnham, J. R. "Experimenter Bias and Lesion Labeling." Unpublished manuscript, Purdue University, 1966.

Cohen, J. *Statistical Power Analysis for the Behavioral Sciences.* (Rev. ed., 1977.) New York: Academic Press, 1969.

Cooper, J., Eisenberg, L., Robert, J., and Dohrenwend, B. S. "The Effect of Experimenter Expectancy and Preparatory Effort on Belief in the Probable Occurrence of Future Events." *Journal of Social Psychology,* 1967, *71,* 221-226.

Elashoff, J. D., and Snow, R. E. "A Case Study in Statistical Inference: Reconsideration of the Rosenthal-Jacobson Data on Teacher Expectancy." Technical Report No. 15, Stanford Center for Research and Development in Teaching, School of Education, Stanford University, December, 1970.

Elashoff, J. D., and Snow, R. E. (Eds.). *Pygmalion Reconsidered.* Worthington, Ohio: Charles A. Jones, 1971.

Jensen, A. R. "How Much Can We Boost IQ and Scholastic Achievement?" *Harvard Educational Review,* 1969, *39,* 1-123.

Miller, K. A. "A Study of 'Experimenter Bias' and 'Subject Awareness' as Demand Characteristic Artifacts in Attitude Change Experiments." Unpublished doctoral dissertation, Bowling Green State University, 1970.

Rosenthal, R. *Experimenter Effects in Behavioral Research.* (Rev. ed., 1976.) New York: Appleton-Century-Crofts, 1966.

Rosenthal, R. "Experimenter Expectancy and the Reassuring Nature of the Null Hypothesis Decision Procedure." *Psychological Bulletin Monograph Supplement,* 1968, *70,* 30-47.

Rosenthal, R. "Empirical Versus Decreed Validation of Clocks and Tests." *American Educational Research Journal,* 1969a, *6,* 689-691.

Rosenthal, R. "Interpersonal Expectations: Effects of the Experimenter's Hypothesis." In R. Rosenthal and R. L. Rosnow (Eds.), *Artifact in Behavioral Research.* New York: Academic Press, 1969.

Rosenthal, R. *On the Social Psychology of the Self-Fulfilling Prophecy: Further Evidence for Pygmalion Effects and Their Mediating Mechanisms.* New York: MSS Modular Publication, Module 53, 1973.

Rosenthal, R. "How Often Are Our Numbers Wrong?" *American Psychologist,* 1978, *33,* 1005-1008.

Rosenthal, R. "The 'File Drawer Problem' and Tolerance for Null Results." *Psychological Bulletin,* 1979a, *86,* 638-641.

Rosenthal, R. (Ed.). *Skill in Nonverbal Communication.* Cambridge, Mass.: Oelgeschlager, Gunn, and Hain, 1979b.

Rosenthal, R., and Fode, K. L. "The Effect of Experimenter Bias on the Performance of the Albino Rat." *Behavioral Science,* 1963, *8,* 183-189.

Rosenthal, R., Hall, J. A., DiMatteo, M. R., Rogers, P. L., and Archer, D. *Sensitivity to Nonverbal Communication: The PONS Test.* Baltimore: The Johns Hopkins University Press, 1979.

Rosenthal, R., and Jacobson, L. *Pygmalion in the Classroom.* New York: Holt, Rinehart and Winston, 1968.

Rosenthal, R., and Lawson, R. "A Longitudinal Study of the Effects of Experimenter Bias on the Operant Learning of Laboratory Rats." *Journal of Psychiatric Research,* 1964, *2,* 61-72.

Rosenthal, R., and Rosnow, R. L. *The Volunteer Subject.* New York: Wiley-Interscience, 1975.

Rosenthal, R., and Rubin, D. B. "Pygmalion Reaffirmed." In J. D. Elashoff and R. E. Snow (Eds.), *Pygmalion Reconsidered.* Worthington, Ohio: Charles A. Jones, 1971.

Rosenthal, R., and Rubin, D. B. "Interpersonal Expectancy Effects: The First 345 Studies." *The Behavioral and Brain Sciences,* 1978, *3,* 377-415.

Rosenthal, R., and Rubin, D. B. "A Simple, General Purpose Index of Magnitude of Experimental Effect." Unpublished manuscript, Harvard University, 1980.

Thorndike, R. L. "Review of Pygmalion in the Classroom." *American Educational Research Journal,* 1968, *5,* 708-711.

Robert Rosenthal is professor of social psychology at Harvard University. His major research interests include interpersonal expectancy effects, nonverbal communication, and social research methods. He is the author of Experimenter Effects in Behavioral Research *and co-author with Lenore Jacobson of* Pygmalion in the Classroom.

Donald B. Rubin is chairman of statistics at Educational Testing Service. His major research interests include: application of Bayes and empirical Bayes statistical techniques; the analysis of data with missing and incomplete observations; the estimation of causal effects in randomized and nonrandomized studies; and handling nonresponse in sample surveys. Currently, he is also serving as coordinating and applications editor for The Journal of the American Statistical Association.

An annotated list of further resources are presented in this chapter.

Sources

Robert Rosenthal
Gene V Glass

Andrews, G., Guitar, B., and Howie, P. "Meta-Analysis of Stuttering Treatment Outcome Studies." *Journal of Speech and Hearing Disorders,* in press.

A meta-analysis showing that treatment for stuttering is effective; mean effect size = 1.3σ.

Cohen, J. *Statistical Power Analysis for the Behavioral Sciences.* New York: Academic Press, 1969. Revised edition, 1977.

A very comprehensive discussion of effect size estimation within a context of statistical power analysis.

Cooper, H. M. "Statistically Combining Independent Studies: A Meta-Analysis of Sex Differences in Conformity." *Journal of Personality and Social Psychology,* 1979, *37,* 131–146.

A meta-analysis showing that, for Asch-type experiments, females conform more than males; mean effect size = .28σ.

Cooper, H. M., and Rosenthal, R. "Statistical Versus Traditional Procedures for Summarizing Research Findings." *Psychological Bulletin,* 1980, *87,* 442–449.

A randomized experiment showing that quantitative research summaries led to greater perception of support for the research hypothesis than did more traditional research summaries.

Glass, G. V, and Smith, M. L. *Meta-Analysis of Research on the Relationship of Class-Size and Achievement.* San Francisco: Far West Laboratory for Educational Research and Development, 1978.

A meta-analysis showing that smaller class size is associated slightly with greater academic achievement; mean effect size = .09σ.

Kavale, K. "The Effectiveness of Psycholinguistic Training: A Meta-Analysis." Unpublished manuscript, University of California, Riverside, 1979.

A meta-analysis showing that psycholinguistic training is effective; mean effect size = .39σ.

Kulik, J. A., Kulik, C. C., and Cohen, P. A. "A Meta-Analysis of Outcome Studies of Keller's Personalized System of Instruction." *American Psychologist,* 1979, *34,* 307-318.

A meta-analysis showing that Keller's personalized system of instruction is effective in improving achievement; mean effect size = .49σ.

Smith, M. L. "Sex Bias in Counseling and Psychotherapy." Unpublished manuscript, University of Colorado, 1978.

A meta-analysis showing little overall sex-bias in counselors' attitudes and behaviors; mean effect size = .04σ.

Smith, M. L., and Glass, G. V. *Relationship of Class-Size to Classroom Processes, Teacher Satisfaction, and Pupil Affect: A Meta-Analysis.* San Francisco: Far West Laboratory for Educational Research and Development, 1979.

A meta-analysis showing that smaller class size is associated with non-achievement benefits; mean effect size = .49σ.

Walberg, H. J., and Haertel, E. (Eds.). *Evaluation in Education: International Progress* (Issue on Research Integration). New York: Pergamon Press, in press.

Includes brief summaries of dozens of meta-analyses of various research domains.

White, K. R. "The Relationship Between Socio-Economic Status and Academic Achievement." Unpublished doctoral dissertation, University of Colorado, 1976.

A meta-analysis showing greater academic achievement by children from higher socio-economic strata; mean effect size = .66σ.

Robert Rosenthal is professor of psychology at Harvard University.

Gene V Glass is professor of education at the University of Colorado.

Index

H

I

J

K

L

M

N

O

New Directions Quarterly Sourcebooks

New Directions for Methodology of Social and Behavioral Science is one of several distinct series of quarterly sourcebooks published by Jossey-Bass. The sourcebooks in each series are designed to serve both as *convenient compendiums* of the latest knowledge and practical experience on their topics and as *long-life reference tools.*

One-year, four-sourcebook subscriptions for each series cost $18 for individuals (when paid by personal check) and $30 for institutions, libraries, and agencies. Single copies of earlier sourcebooks are available at $6.95 each *prepaid* (or $7.95 each when *billed*).

A complete listing is given below of current and past sourcebooks in the *New Directions for Methodology of Social and Behavioral Science* series. The titles and editors-in-chief of the other series are also listed. To subscribe, or to receive further information, write: New Directions Subscriptions, Jossey-Bass Inc., Publishers, 433 California Street, San Francisco, California 94104.

New Directions for Methodology of Social and Behavioral Science
Donald W. Fiske, Editor-in-Chief
1979–1980:
1. *Unobtrusive Measurement Today,* Lee Sechrest
2. *Methods for Studying Person-Situation Interactions,* Lynn R. Kahle
3. *Realizations of Brunswik's Representative Design,* Kenneth R. Hammond, Nancy E. Wascoe
4. *Fallible Judgment in Behavioral Research,* Richard A. Shweder

New Directions for Child Development
William Damon, Editor-in-Chief

New Directions for College Learning Assistance
Kurt V. Lauridsen, Editor-in-Chief

New Directions for Community Colleges
Arthur M. Cohen, Editor-in-Chief
Florence B. Brawer, Associate Editor

New Directions for Continuing Education
Alan B. Knox, Editor-in-Chief

New Directions for Exceptional Children
James J. Gallagher, Editor-in-Chief

New Directions for Experiential Learning
Morris T. Keeton and Pamela J. Tate, Editors-in-Chief

New Directions for Higher Education
JB Lon Hefferlin, Editor-in-Chief

New Directions for Institutional Advancement
A. Westley Rowland, Editor-in-Chief

New Directions for Institutional Research
Marvin W. Peterson, Editor-in-Chief

New Directions for Mental Health Services
H. Richard Lamb, Editor-in-Chief

New Directions for Program Evaluation
Scarvia B. Anderson, Editor-in-Chief

New Directions for Student Services
Ursula Delworth and Gary R. Hanson, Editors-in-Chief

New Directions for Teaching and Learning
Kenneth E. Eble and John Noonan, Editors-in-Chief

New Directions for Testing and Measurement
William B. Schrader, Editor-in-Chief

From the Editor's Notes

In the social and behavioral sciences, it has become almost obligatory to end reports with clarion calls for further research. Yet we have been better at issuing such calls than at knowing what to do with the answers. There are several areas of these fields in which we have the combined results of several studies all addressing the same question, and where significant summaries can effectively be made. It is the purpose of this volume of New Directions for Methodology of Social and Behavioral Science *to make available various procedures developed for the quantitative assessment of numbers of studies in particular research domains. It is our hope that this volume will contribute to the trend toward more rigorous summarization and integration of findings, providing at least an estimate of overall effect size, a combined probability level, a statement of tolerance for future null results, and indications of possible moderator variables affecting the size of the effect.*

JOSSEY-BASS